REVISE EDEXCEL

AS Mathematics
C1 C2 M1 S1 D1

D0531051

REVISION WORKBOOK

Authors: Su Nicholson and Glyn Payne

A note from the publisher

In order to ensure that this resource offers high-quality support for the associated Edexcel qualification, it has been through a review process by the awarding body to confirm that it fully covers the teaching and learning content of the specification or part of a specification at which it is aimed, and demonstrates an appropriate balance between the development of subject skills, knowledge and understanding, in addition to preparation for assessment.

While the publishers have made every attempt to ensure that advice on the qualification and its assessment is accurate, the official specification and associated assessment guidance materials are the only authoritative source of information and should always be referred to for definitive guidance.

Edexcel examiners have not contributed to any sections in this resource relevant to examination papers for which they have responsibility.

No material from an endorsed resource will be used verbatim in any assessment set by Edexcel.

Endorsement of a resource does not mean that the resource is required to achieve this Edexcel qualification, nor does it mean that it is the only suitable material available to support the qualification, and any resource lists produced by the awarding body shall include this and other appropriate resources.

For the full range of Pearson revision titles across GCSE, BTEC and AS Level visit:

www.pearsonschools.co.uk/revise

ALWAYS LEARNING

PEARSON

Contents

A small bit of small print

Edexcel publishes Sample Assessment Material and the Specification on its website. This is the official content and this book should be used in conjunction with it. The questions in this book have been written to help you practise every topic in the book. Remember: the real exam questions may not look like this.

Mathematical Formulae and Statistical Tables

The Mathematical Formulae and Statistical Tables that you need for your exams is available from the Edexcel website.

Index laws

1. Find the value of $25^{-\frac{3}{2}}$ (2)

....

....

Guided 2. Express $\sqrt{3}\left(27^{\frac{2}{3}}\right)$ in the form 3^x (2)

$\sqrt{3}\left(27^{\frac{2}{3}}\right) = 3^{\cdots} \times (27^{\cdots})^2 =$ .... = ...

3. Simplify $3x\left(2x^{-\frac{3}{4}}\right)$ (2)

....

4. Simplify $\dfrac{20x^{\frac{5}{3}}}{4x}$ (2)

....

Guided 5. Simplify fully $\dfrac{\left(3x^{\frac{1}{2}}\right)^3}{9x^3}$ (3)

$\dfrac{\left(3x^{\frac{1}{2}}\right)^3}{9x^3} = \dfrac{\cdots\cdots\cdots\cdots}{9x^3} =$ .... = ...

> First simplify the numerator.

6. Write $\dfrac{3 - x^{\frac{3}{2}}}{\sqrt{x}}$ in the form $3x^p - x^q$ where p and q are constants. (2)

....

....

7. Solve $3^{2x+1} \times 9^x = 27$ (2)

....

....

....

> Write both sides of the equation as powers of 3 to find x.

8. Solve $2^{2x-3} \times 4^{x+2} = 8$ (4)

....

....

....

Expanding and factorising

Guided **1.** Expand $(x - 1)(x + 2)^2$ (2)

$(x - 1)(x + 2)^2 = (x - 1)(x^2 \underline{\hspace{2cm}})$

....

....

> First expand $(x + 2)^2$.

> Multiply out and collect like terms, then multiply by $(x - 1)$.

Guided **2.** Factorise completely $x^3 - 9x$ (3)

$x^3 - 9x = x(x^2 \underline{\hspace{1cm}})$

....

....

> First take out the common factor. Then factorise the expression inside the brackets.

3. Expand $(x - 4)(x + 2)(x - 1)$ (2)

....

....

....

4. Factorise completely $x^3 + 4x^2 - 5x$ (3)

....

....

....

5. Show that $(2 - 3\sqrt{x})^2$ can be written as $4 - k\sqrt{x} + 9x$, where k is a constant. (2)

....

....

....

6. Given $f(x) = (x^2 - 4x)(x + 3) + 6x$

(a) express $f(x)$ in the form $x(ax^2 + bx + c)$ where a, b and c are constants. (3)

....

....

....

(b) Hence factorise $f(x)$ completely. (2)

....

....

Surds

1. Write $\sqrt{72}$ in the form $a\sqrt{2}$ where a is an integer.   (2)

....

> **Guided**

2. Simplify $\sqrt{18} + \sqrt{50}$ giving your answer in the form $a\sqrt{b}$ where a and b are integers.   (2)

$$\sqrt{18} + \sqrt{50} = \sqrt{9 \times 2} + \sqrt{25 \times 2}$$

$$= 3 \times \sqrt{2} + \text{.........................}$$

....

> **Guided**

3. Simplify $\dfrac{\sqrt{5} + 3}{\sqrt{5} - 2}$ in the form $a + b\sqrt{5}$ where a and b are integers.   (4)

Insert brackets and rationalise the denominator.

Multiply out the brackets in the numerator and the denominator.

$$\frac{\sqrt{5} + 3}{\sqrt{5} - 2} = \frac{(\sqrt{5} + 3)(\sqrt{5} \text{ ....})}{(\sqrt{5} - 2)(\sqrt{5} \text{ ....})}$$

....

....

....

....

4. Express $\sqrt{75} + \dfrac{21}{\sqrt{3}}$ in the form $a\sqrt{3}$ where a is an integer.   (3)

....

Rationalise the denominator in the second term.

....

....

5. Express $(9 + \sqrt{8})(3 - \sqrt{2})$ in the form $a + b\sqrt{2}$ where a and b are integers.   (3)

....

....

6. Express $(7 - \sqrt{3})^2$ in the form $a + b\sqrt{3}$ where a and b are integers.   (3)

....

....

7. Write $\dfrac{3(2 - \sqrt{5})}{(2 + \sqrt{5})}$ in the form $a\sqrt{5} + b$ where a and b are integers.   (5)

....

....

....

Quadratic equations

1. Solve $3(x − 1)^2 + 8x − 11 = 0$ **(1)**

....

....

....

....

Guided 2. Given that $f(x) = x^2 − 10x + 15$

(a) express $f(x)$ in the form $(x + a)^2 + b$ where a and b are integers.   **(3)**

$x^2 − 10x + 15 = (x \text{ .... })^2 − \text{ .... } + 15$ | $2a = −10$ |

$= \text{ .... }$ | Subtract a^2. |

....

(b) Hence, or otherwise, show that the roots of $x^2 − 10x + 15 = 0$ are $c \pm d\sqrt{10}$,
where c and d are integers to be found.   **(3)**

$(x \text{ .... })^2 − \text{ .... } = 0$ | Rearrange into completed square form then square root both sides. |

$(x \text{ .... })^2 \qquad = \text{ .... }$

$(x \text{ .... }) \qquad = \text{ .... }$ | Any positive number has two square roots. |

....

....

....

3. $8x − 6 − x^2 = q − (x + p)^2$ where p and q are integers. Find the values of p and q.   **(3)**

....

....

....

....

....

....

4. $3x^2 + 6x + 5 = a(x + b)^2 + c$

Find the values of the constants a, b and c.   **(3)**

....

....

....

....

The discriminant

> **Guided** 1. The equation $x^2 - 2px + p = 0$, where p is a non-zero constant, has equal roots. Find the value of p. **(4)**

$a = 1, b = -2p, c = $ .... | Identify the values of a, b and c.

$b^2 - 4ac = (-2p)^2 - 4 \times 1 \times$ .... | For equal roots $b^2 - 4ac = 0$. Then solve to find p.

....

....

....

> **Guided** 2. The equation $3x^2 + kx - 5 = k$ has no real solutions for x. Show that $k^2 + 12k + 60 < 0$ **(3)**

$3x^2 + kx - 5$ .... $= 0$ | Write in the form $ax^2 + bx + c = 0$ before identifying the values of a, b and c.

$a = 3, b = k, c = $ ....

$b^2 - 4ac = (k)^2 - 4 \times 3 \times$ .... | For no real roots $b^2 - 4ac < 0$.

....

....

3. Find the value of the discriminant of $3x - 7 - x^2$ **(2)**

....

....

....

4. $f(x) = x^2 + (p - 4)x - 3p$ where p is a constant.

(a) Find the discriminant of $f(x)$ in terms of p. **(2)**

....

....

....

(b) Show that the discriminant can be written in the form $(x + a)^2 + b$ where a and b are integers to be found. **(2)**

....

....

....

(c) Show that, for all values of p, the equation $f(x) = 0$ has distinct real roots. **(2)**

....

....

....

Sketching quadratics

Guided 1. Sketch the curve with equation $y = (x - 3)(x + 2)$, showing clearly the coordinates of any points where the curve crosses the coordinate axes. **(3)**

When $x = 0$, $y = (0 - 3)(0 + 2)$

$= \ldots\ldots\ldots\ldots$

When $y = 0$, $0 = (x - 3)(x + 2)$

so $x = \ldots\ldots\ldots\ldots$ or $x = \ldots\ldots\ldots\ldots$

> The curve crosses the x-axis when $y = 0$
> and it crosses the y-axis when $x = 0$.

Guided 2. (a) Sketch the curve with equation $y = (x + 3)^2 + 4$, showing clearly the coordinates of any points where the curve crosses the coordinate axes. **(3)**

The coordinates of the vertex

are ($\ldots\ldots\ldots\ldots$, $\ldots\ldots\ldots\ldots$)

When $x = 0$, $y = (0 + 3)^2 + 4$

$= \ldots\ldots\ldots\ldots$

> The curve with equation $y = (x + a)^2 + b$
> has a **vertex** at $(-a, b)$.

(b) Find the value of the discriminant of $(x + 3)^2 + 4$.
Explain how the sign of the discriminant relates to your sketch in part (a). **(2)**

$\ldots\ldots\ldots\ldots\ldots\ldots\ldots\ldots\ldots\ldots\ldots\ldots\ldots\ldots\ldots\ldots\ldots\ldots\ldots\ldots\ldots\ldots\ldots\ldots\ldots\ldots\ldots\ldots\ldots\ldots\ldots\ldots\ldots\ldots\ldots\ldots\ldots\ldots$

$\ldots\ldots\ldots\ldots\ldots\ldots\ldots\ldots\ldots\ldots\ldots\ldots\ldots\ldots\ldots\ldots\ldots\ldots\ldots\ldots\ldots\ldots\ldots\ldots\ldots\ldots\ldots\ldots\ldots\ldots\ldots\ldots\ldots\ldots\ldots\ldots\ldots\ldots$

$\ldots\ldots\ldots\ldots\ldots\ldots\ldots\ldots\ldots\ldots\ldots\ldots\ldots\ldots\ldots\ldots\ldots\ldots\ldots\ldots\ldots\ldots\ldots\ldots\ldots\ldots\ldots\ldots\ldots\ldots\ldots\ldots\ldots\ldots\ldots\ldots\ldots\ldots$

> The discriminant tells you
> about the nature of the **roots**,
> which are the points where
> the curve crosses the x-axis.

$\ldots\ldots\ldots\ldots\ldots\ldots\ldots\ldots\ldots\ldots\ldots\ldots\ldots\ldots\ldots\ldots\ldots\ldots\ldots\ldots\ldots\ldots\ldots\ldots\ldots\ldots\ldots\ldots\ldots\ldots\ldots\ldots\ldots\ldots\ldots\ldots\ldots\ldots\ldots\ldots\ldots\ldots\ldots\ldots\ldots\ldots\ldots\ldots\ldots\ldots\ldots\ldots\ldots$

3. Sketch the curve with equation $y = x(5 - x)$, showing clearly the coordinates of any points where the curve crosses the coordinate axes. **(3)**

$\ldots\ldots\ldots\ldots\ldots\ldots\ldots\ldots\ldots\ldots\ldots\ldots\ldots\ldots\ldots\ldots\ldots\ldots\ldots\ldots\ldots\ldots\ldots\ldots\ldots\ldots\ldots\ldots\ldots\ldots\ldots\ldots$

$\ldots\ldots\ldots\ldots\ldots\ldots\ldots\ldots\ldots\ldots\ldots\ldots\ldots\ldots\ldots\ldots\ldots\ldots\ldots\ldots\ldots\ldots\ldots\ldots\ldots\ldots\ldots\ldots\ldots$

$\ldots\ldots\ldots\ldots\ldots\ldots\ldots\ldots\ldots\ldots\ldots\ldots\ldots\ldots\ldots\ldots\ldots\ldots\ldots\ldots\ldots\ldots\ldots\ldots\ldots\ldots\ldots\ldots\ldots$

$\ldots\ldots\ldots\ldots\ldots\ldots\ldots\ldots\ldots\ldots\ldots\ldots\ldots\ldots\ldots\ldots\ldots\ldots\ldots\ldots\ldots\ldots\ldots$

$\ldots\ldots\ldots\ldots\ldots\ldots\ldots\ldots\ldots\ldots\ldots\ldots\ldots\ldots\ldots\ldots\ldots\ldots\ldots\ldots\ldots\ldots\ldots\ldots$

Had a go ☐ Nearly there ☐ Nailed it! ☐

Simultaneous equations

> **Guided**

1. Solve the simultaneous equations

$$x - y = 3 \qquad ①$$
$$x^2 - 2y = 6 \qquad ② \qquad \textbf{(7)}$$

$$y = \text{.....................} \qquad ③$$

$$x^2 - 2(\text{.................}) = 6$$

$$\text{.................................} = 6$$

$$\text{.................................} = 0$$

....

....

....

> Number the equations to keep track of your working.

> Rearrange ① to write y in terms of x and substitute in ②.

> Solve the quadratic to find the two values of x.
> Substitute into ③ to find the corresponding values of y.

2. Solve the simultaneous equations

$$x = y + 3$$
$$x^2 + y^2 = 17 \qquad \textbf{(7)}$$

....

....

....

....

....

....

3. (a) By eliminating y from the equations

$$y = x + 8$$
$$xy + 3x^2 = 16$$

show that

$$x^2 + 2x - 4 = 0 \qquad \textbf{(2)}$$

....

....

....

....

(b) Hence, or otherwise, solve the simultaneous equations

$$y = x + 8$$
$$xy + 3x^2 = 16$$

giving your answers in the form $a \pm b\sqrt{5}$, where a and b are integers. **(5)**

....

....

....

Inequalities

> **Guided**

1. Find the set of values of x for which

(a) $2(x - 3) < 4 - 3x$ **(2)**

$2x - 6 < 4 - 3x$

> Expand the brackets and rearrange to make x the subject.

$5x < $ .... so $x < $ ....

(b) $(2x - 5)(2 + x) < 0$ **(3)**

> Make equal to zero and solve to find where the graph of $y = (2x - 5)(2 + x)$ crosses the x-axis.

$(2x - 5)(2 + x) = 0$

So $x = $ .... or $x = $ ....

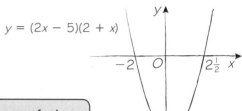

$y = (2x - 5)(2 + x)$

> Identify the range of values of x which makes $y < 0$.

....

(c) **both** $2(x - 3) < 4 - 3x$ **and** $(2x - 5)(2 + x) < 0$ **(1)**

> The values where the inequalities **overlap** are the values which satisfy them both.

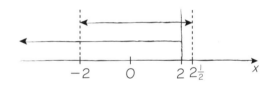

.... $< x < $ ....

2. Find the set of values of x for which

$x^2 - 8x + 15 \geqslant 0$ **(4)**

....

....

....

....

3. The equation $x^2 + 2kx + (3 - 2k) = 0$, where k is a constant, has different real roots.

(a) Show that $k^2 + 2k - 3 > 0$ **(2)**

....

....

....

....

....

(b) Find the set of possible values of k. **(4)**

....

....

....

Sketching cubics

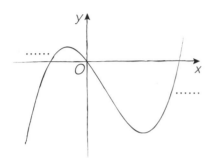

> **Guided** 1. The curve C has the equation $y = x(x + 2)(x - 5)$. Sketch C, showing clearly the coordinates of the points where the curve meets the coordinate axes. **(4)**

When $y = 0$, $0 = x(x + 2)(x - 5)$ so $x = \text{......}$ or $x = \text{......}$ or $x = \text{......}$

The curve crosses the x-axis at the values of x which make each factor equal to 0.

As x is a factor of $x(x + 2)(x - 5)$, the curve C will pass through the origin.

> **Guided** 2. The curve C has the equation $y = (x + 1)^2(3 - x)$. Sketch C, showing clearly the coordinates of the points where the curve meets the coordinate axes. **(4)**

When $y = 0$, $0 = (x + 1)^2(3 - x)$ $x = \text{......}$ or $x = \text{......}$

When $x = 0$, $y = (0 + 1)^2(3 - 0) = \text{......}$

As the factor $(x + 1)$ is repeated, the curve touches the x-axis at $x = -1$.

Work out the point where the curve crosses the y-axis by setting $x = 0$.

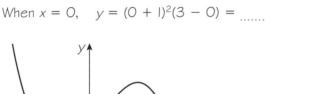

As the coefficient of x^3 is negative, the shape of the curve will be 'upside down'.

3. The curve C has the equation $y = (x - 1)(x + 2)(x - 4)$. Sketch C, showing clearly the coordinates of the points where the curve meets the coordinate axes. **(4)**

....

....

....

4. Factorise completely $9x - x^3$. Hence sketch the curve with equation $y = 9x - x^3$ **(6)**

....

....

....

Transformations 1

 1. The diagram shows a sketch of a curve with equation $y = f(x)$. The curve has a maximum point at $(-2, 4)$ and a minimum point at $(0, 0)$.

On the same diagram, sketch the curve with equation

(a) $f(x - 2)$ **(3)**

> $f(x + a)$ is a translation of $f(x)$ by $\begin{pmatrix} -a \\ 0 \end{pmatrix}$

(b) $f(-x)$ **(3)**

> $f(-x)$ is a reflection of $f(x)$ in the y-axis.

On each sketch, show clearly the coordinates of the maximum and minimum points and any points of intersection with the axes.

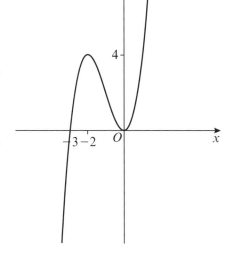

 2. The diagram shows a sketch of a curve with equation $y = f(x)$.
The curve has a minimum point at $(4, -16)$.
On separate diagrams, sketch the curve with equation

(a) $y = 3f(x)$ **(3)**

> $af(x)$ is a stretch, factor a, of $f(x)$ in the y-direction.

(b) $y = -f(x)$ **(3)**

> $-f(x)$ is a reflection of $f(x)$ in the x-axis.

(c) $y = f(2x)$ **(3)**

> $f(ax)$ is a stretch, factor $\dfrac{1}{a}$, of $f(x)$ in the x-direction.

On each sketch, show clearly the coordinates of the minimum point and any points of intersection with the axes.

The curve with equation $y = f(x + k)$ has a minimum point on the y-axis.

(d) What is the value of k?   **(1)**

....

Transformations 2

> **Guided**

1. The diagram shows a sketch of part of the curve with equation $y = f(x)$

The curve has a minimum point $(2, -5)$ and an asymptote $y = -1$

On separate diagrams, sketch the curve with equation

(a) $y = f(x) + 3$ **(2)**

(b) $y = 3f(x)$ **(2)**

(c) $y = f(x - 1)$ **(3)**

On each diagram, show clearly the coordinates of the minimum point and the asymptote with its equation.

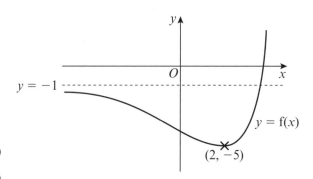

> The asymptote is horizontal so it is only transformed by a transformation in the y-direction.

> **Guided**

2. The diagram shows a sketch of the curve with equation $y = f(x)$ where $f(x) = \dfrac{3x}{x - 1}, x \neq 1$

The curve has asymptotes with equations $y = 3$ and $x = 1$

(a) Sketch the curve with equation $y = f(x - 3)$ and state the equations of its asymptotes.   **(3)**

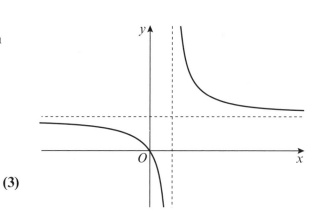

(b) Find the coordinates of the points where the curve with equation $y = f(x - 3)$ crosses the coordinate axes.   **(3)**

> Replace x with $x - 3$ in the equation, then find x when $f(x - 3) = 0$ and $f(x - 3)$ when $x = 0$.

$f(x - 3) = \dfrac{3(x - 3)}{(x - 3) - 1} = $ ....

....

....

Sketching $y = \dfrac{k}{x}$

1. The diagram shows a sketch of the curve with equation $y = \dfrac{4}{x}, \ x \neq 0$

(a) On a separate diagram, sketch the curve with equation $y = \dfrac{4}{x-1}, \ x \neq 1$, showing any asymptotes and the coordinates of any point at which the curve crosses a coordinate axis. **(3)**

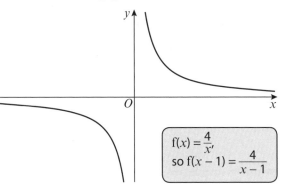

$f(x) = \dfrac{4}{x}$, so $f(x-1) = \dfrac{4}{x-1}$

(b) Write down the equations of the asymptotes of the curve in part (a). **(2)**

....

2. The diagram shows a sketch of the curve with equation $y = \dfrac{5}{x}, \ x \neq 0$

(a) On a separate diagram, sketch the curve with equation $y = \dfrac{5}{x} + 3, \ x \neq 0$, showing any asymptotes and the coordinates of any point at which the curve crosses a coordinate axis. **(3)**

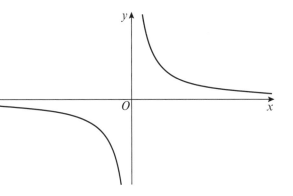

(b) Write down the equations of the asymptotes of the curve in part (a). **(2)**

....

Intersecting graphs

> **Guided**

1. The curve C has equation $y = -\dfrac{3}{x}$ and the line l has equation $x + y + 2 = 0$

   (a) On the same axes, sketch the graphs of C and l, indicating clearly the coordinates of any intersections with the axes. **(3)**

   ....

   ....

   ....

   ....

   ....

   ....

   (b) Find the coordinates of the points of intersection of C and l. **(6)**

   $y = -x - 2$

   $-\dfrac{3}{x} = -x - 2$

   > Rearrange the linear equation to $y = -x - 2$.
   > The x-coordinates at the points of intersection are the solutions to the equation $-\dfrac{3}{x} = -x - 2$.

   ....

   ....

   ....

   ....

2. (a) On the same axes, sketch the graph of the curve with equation

   (i) $y = x^2(x + 2)$

   (ii) $y = x(4 - x)$

   and indicate on your sketches the coordinates of all the points where the curves cross the x-axis. **(6)**

   ....

   ....

   ....

   ....

   ....

   (b) Use algebra to find the coordinates of the points where the graphs intersect. **(7)**

   ....

   ....

   ....

   ....

   ....

   ....

   ....

Equations of lines

1. The line L has equation $y = 7 - 3x$

    Show that the point $(3, -2)$ lies on L. **(1)**

    ....

> **Guided**

2. The line L has equation $2x + 7y - 3 = 0$

    Find the gradient of L. **(2)**

    > Rearrange the equation to make y the subject.

    > The equation of a straight line can be written in the form $y = mx + c$, where m is the gradient of the line, and c is the point where it crosses the y-axis.

    $7y =$ ....

    $y =$ ....

    Gradient = ...

> **Guided**

3. The line L passes through the point A $(3, -2)$ and has gradient $-\frac{1}{3}$

    Find an equation of L, giving your answer in the form $y = mx + c$ **(3)**

    > If a straight line has gradient m and passes through the point (x_1, y_1), then you can write its equation as $y - y_1 = m(x - x_1)$.

    > Remember to write the answer in the form asked for in the question.

    $x_1 =$ .... $y_1 =$ .... $m =$ ....

    $y -$ ...... = ... $(x -$ ......$)$

    ....

    ....

> **Guided**

4. The points A $(-2, 1)$ and B $(6, -2)$ lie on the line L.

    (a) Find the gradient of the line L. **(2)**

    > If a straight line has gradient m and passes through the points (x_1, y_1) and (x_2, y_2), then $m = \dfrac{y_2 - y_1}{x_2 - x_1}$

    $x_1 =$ ...... $y_1 =$ ...... $x_2 =$ ...... $y_2 =$ ......

    $m = \dfrac{y_2 - y_1}{x_2 - x_1} =$

    (b) Find an equation for L in the form $ax + by + c = 0$, where a, b and c are integers. **(2)**

    ....

    ....

    ....

5. (a) The line L has equation $3y = 4x + p$. The point A $(2, 3)$ lies on L.

    Find the value of the constant p. **(1)**

    ....

    (b) Find an equation for the straight line joining the points A $(2, 3)$ and B $(-1, 7)$ in the form $ax + by + c = 0$, where a, b and c are integers. **(4)**

    ....

    ....

    ....

    ....

Parallel and perpendicular

> **Guided**   1.   The line L has equation $y = 4 - 3x$

   (a) Show that the point P $(3, -5)$ lies on L.   **(1)**

   ....

   (b) Find an equation of the line perpendicular to L,
   which passes through P.
   Give your answer in the form $ax + by + c = 0$,
   where a, b and c are integers.   **(4)**

   > If the gradient of one line is a fraction, the gradient of a perpendicular line is found by turning the fraction upside down and changing the sign.

   Gradient of L = ...

   Gradient of perpendicular line = ...

   Equation of perpendicular line through $(3, -5)$ is ....

   ....

   ....

> **Guided**   2.   The points P and Q have coordinates $(-2, 5)$ and $(6, 3)$ respectively.

   (a) Find the coordinates of the midpoint of PQ.   **(1)**

   Coordinates of midpoint are

   $\left(\dfrac{-2 + 6}{2}, \dfrac{................}{2}\right) = $ ....

   > The coordinates of the midpoint of the line joining the points (x_1, y_1) and (x_2, y_2) are $\left(\dfrac{x_1 + x_2}{2}, \dfrac{y_1 + y_2}{2}\right)$.

   (b) The line l is perpendicular to PQ and passes through the midpoint of PQ.
   Find an equation for l, giving your answer in the form $ax + by + c = 0$,
   where a, b and c are integers.   **(4)**

   ....

   ....

   ....

   ....

3.   The line l_1 has equation $3x + 4y - 5 = 0$

   (a) Find the gradient of l_1.   **(2)**

   ....

   ....

   The line l_2 is perpendicular to l_1 and passes through the point $(1, 3)$.

   (b) Find the equation of l_2 in the form $y = mx + c$, where m and c are constants.   **(3)**

   ....

   ....

   ....

   ....

Lengths and areas

1. A is the point $(-1, 6)$ and B is the point $(3, -2)$.
   The length of AB is $p\sqrt{5}$, where p is an integer.
   Find the value of p. **(3)**

   > Draw a sketch showing the positions of points A and B and use Pythagoras' theorem.

   ....

   ....

   ....

   ....

> **Guided**

2. The line l_1 has equation $y = x + 1$
   The line l_2 has equation $x + 3y - 15 = 0$
   l_1 and l_2 intersect at the point A.

   (a) Find the coordinates of A. **(3)**

   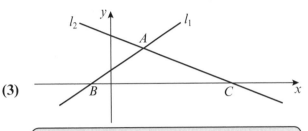

   $x + 3(x + 1) - 15 = 0$

   $x + 3x +$ ....

   > Start by solving the equations simultaneously.

   ....

   ....

   l_1 crosses the x-axis at the point B.
   l_2 crosses the x-axis at the point C.

   (b) Find the area of triangle ABC. **(3)**

   > Substitute $y = 0$ into the equations to find the x-coordinates of B and C, then use Area $= \frac{1}{2} \times$ base $\times$ height.

   ....

   ....

   ....

   ....

3. The line l_1 has equation $y = 2x + 8$
   The line l_2 is perpendicular to l_1 and passes through the point $(3\frac{1}{2}, 0)$.
   Find the area of the triangle formed by the lines l_1, l_2 and the x-axis. **(9)**

   ....

   ....

   ....

   ....

   ....

   ....

   ....

   ....

Arithmetic sequences

> **Guided**   **1.** The nth term of an arithmetic sequence is $(3n - 2)$.

(a) Write down the first three terms of this series. **(2)**

| To find the first three terms, substitute $n = 1, 2$ and 3 into the formula for the nth term. |

First term $n = 1$ $3 \times 1 - 2$ $= \dots\dots\dots$

Second term $n = 2$ $3 \times \dots\dots$ $= \dots\dots$

Third term $\dots\dots$ $\dots\dots\dots$ $= \dots\dots$

(b) State the value of the common difference. **(1)**

| The common difference is the difference between any two consecutive terms in the sequence. |

....

> **Guided**   **2.** The first term of an arithmetic sequence is 40 and the common difference is -2.5

(a) Find the value of the 20th term. **(2)**

| The general formula for the nth term of an arithmetic sequence is $a + (n - 1)d$. |

$a = \dots\dots$ $d = \dots\dots$

20th term $= a + (20 - 1)d = \dots\dots\dots\dots = \dots\dots\dots\dots$

The rth term of the sequence is 0

(b) Find the value of r. **(2)**

....

....

3. The first term of an arithmetic series is a and the common difference is d.
The 15th term of the series is 9 and the 20th term of the series is $16\frac{1}{2}$

(a) Use this information to write down two equations for a and d. **(2)**

....

....

(b) Find the values of a and d. **(2)**

....

....

....

4. Matt prepares for a cycling holiday by cycling on each of 10 consecutive days. On each day after the first day he cycles further than he cycled on the previous day. The 10 distances he cycles form an arithmetic sequence with first term a miles and common difference d miles.
Matt cycles 60 miles on the 5th day and 85 miles on the 10th day.
Find the value of a and the value of d. **(7)**

....

....

....

....

Recurrence relationships

Guided   **1.** A sequence $a_1, a_2, a_3, \ldots$ is defined by

$$a_1 = 2$$
$$a_{n+1} = 2a_n - 3, \ n \geqslant 1$$

(a) Find the value of a_2 and the value of a_3.   **(2)**

$$a_1 = 2$$
$$a_2 = 2a_1 - 3 = \ \ldots\ldots\ldots\ldots\ldots$$
$$a_3 = 2a_2 - 3 = \ \ldots\ldots\ldots\ldots\ldots$$

> The recurrence relationship tells you how to find each term in the sequence from the previous term.

(b) Calculate the value of $\sum\limits_{r=1}^{5} a_r$ **(3)**

> The Σ symbol means 'sum of'. You need to work out $a_1 + a_2 + a_3 + a_4 + a_5$.

$$a_4 = \ \ldots\ldots\ldots\ldots\ldots \qquad a_5 = \ \ldots\ldots\ldots\ldots\ldots$$

$$a_1 + a_2 + a_3 + a_4 + a_5 = \ \ldots\ldots\ldots\ldots\ldots\ldots\ldots\ldots\ldots\ldots \quad = \ \ldots\ldots\ldots\ldots\ldots\ldots\ldots\ldots$$

2. A sequence $a_1, a_2, a_3, \ldots$ is defined by

$$a_1 = k$$
$$a_{n+1} = 3a_n - 2, \ n \geqslant 1$$

where k is a positive integer.

(a) Write down an expression for a_2 in terms of k.   **(1)**

....

(b) Show that $a_3 = 9k - 8$ **(2)**

....

(c) Given that $\sum\limits_{r=1}^{4} a_r = 44,$ find the value of k.   **(4)**

....

....

....

....

3. A sequence $x_1, x_2, x_3, \ldots$ is defined by

$$x_1 = 1$$
$$x_{n+1} = px_n + 3, \ n \geqslant 1$$

where p is a constant.

(a) Write down an expression for x_2 in terms of p.   **(1)**

....

(b) Show that $x_3 = p^2 + 3p + 3$ **(2)**

....

(c) Given that $x_3 = 31,$ find the possible values of p.   **(3)**

....

....

Arithmetic series

Guided　**1.** Find the sum of the arithmetic sequence $-8, -5, -2, ..., 19$　(3)

$a =$ ....　$d =$ ....

$a + (n - 1)d = 19$

> To find the number of terms, n, solve $a + (n - 1)d = 19$, then use $S_n = \frac{1}{2}n[2a + (n - 1)d]$.

.... $= 19$

....

....

2. Find the sum of the odd numbers from 1 to 99 inclusive.

$1 + 3 + 5 + ... + 99$　(3)

....

....

....

Guided　**3.** An arithmetic series has first term a and common difference d. The sum of the first 10 terms of the series is 150

> Use $S_n = \frac{1}{2}n[2a + (n - 1)d]$ and write in simplest form.

(a) Show that $2a + 9d = 30$　(2)

$S_{10} =$

....

Given also that the 5th term of the sequence is 14

(b) write down a second equation in a and d　(1)

....

(c) find the value of a and the value of d.　(4)　| Solve the two equations simultaneously. |

....

....

4. An arithmetic series has first term 149 and common difference -2. The sum of the first n terms of the series is 5000

(a) Form an equation in n, and show that your equation may be written as
$n^2 - 150n + 5000 = 0$　(3)

....

....

....

(b) Solve the equation in part (a).　(3)

....

....

Sequence and series problems

Guided 1. Kelly pays into a savings scheme. In the first year she pays £600. Her payments then increase by £100 each year so she pays £700 in the second year, £800 in the third year and so on.

(a) Find the amount that Kelly will pay in the 25th year. **(2)**

$a = $ .... $d = $ ....

> This is an arithmetic sequence. Use the formula for the nth term, $u_n = a + (n-1)d$.

25th year = ...

(b) Find the total amount that Kelly will pay in over the 25 years. **(2)**

$S_{25} = $ ....

> Find the sum of the first 25 terms. Use $S_n = \frac{1}{2}n[2a + (n-1)d]$.

....

....

Guided 2. Micah saves some money each week over a period of w weeks. He saves 50p in week 1, 60p in week 2, 70p in week 3 and so on, so that his weekly savings form an arithmetic sequence. Micah saves a total of £121.50 over the period of w weeks.

> Use $S_n = \frac{1}{2}n[2a + (n-1)d]$. Remember to work with consistent units.

Show that $w(w + 9) = 45 \times 54$ and hence write down the value of w. **(5)**

$a = $ .... $d = $ ....

$S_w = \frac{1}{2}w($ .... $)$

....

....

....

3. A company, which makes racing bikes, plans to increase its production.

The number of racing bikes produced is to be increased by 10 each week from 150 in week 1 to 160 in week 2, to 170 in week 3 and so on, until it is producing 500 in week N.

(a) Find the value of N. **(2)**

....

....

The company plans to continue to produce 500 racing bikes each week.

(b) Find the total number of racing bikes that will be made in the first 52 weeks starting from and including week 1. **(5)**

....

....

....

....

Differentiation 1

1. The curve C has equation $y = 5x - 3x^{\frac{3}{2}} + 4x^3$, $x > 0$

    Find an expression for $\dfrac{dy}{dx}$ **(3)**

    > If $y = ax^n$, then $\dfrac{dy}{dx} = anx^{n-1}$.

    ....

    ....

Guided

2. Given $y = 5x^2 + \dfrac{2}{x} - \dfrac{3}{x^2}$, $x \neq 0$, find $\dfrac{dy}{dx}$ **(3)**

    > Write every term in the polynomial in the form ax^n before differentiating.

    $y = 5x^2 + 2x^{\cdots\cdots} - 3x^{\cdots\cdots}$

    $\dfrac{dy}{dx} = $ ....

Guided

3. Differentiate $\dfrac{3x - 2\sqrt{x}}{x}$, $x \neq 0$, with respect to x.   **(3)**

    > Divide each term by x and write in the form ax^n before differentiating. Remember that $\sqrt{x} = x^{\frac{1}{2}}$.

    $f(x) = \dfrac{3x - 2\sqrt{x}}{x} = \dfrac{3x}{x} - \dfrac{2\sqrt{x}}{x} = $ ....

    > Constant terms differentiate to zero.

    $f'(x) = $ ....

    ....

4. (a) Write $\dfrac{5x^{\frac{1}{3}} - 2}{x}$ in the form $5x^p - 2x^q$, where p and q are constants.   **(2)**

    ....

    ....

    Given that $y = 4x - 9 + \dfrac{5x^{\frac{1}{3}} - 2}{x}$, $x > 0$

    (b) find $\dfrac{dy}{dx}$ **(4)**

    ....

    ....

    ....

    ....

5. Given $f(x) = \dfrac{(4 + \sqrt{x})^2}{x}$, $x \neq 0$, find $f'(x)$.   **(4)**

    ....

    ....

    ....

    ....

    ....

    ....

Differentiation 2

1. Given that $y = 4x^3 - 3x + 5$, find

   (a) $\dfrac{\mathrm{d}y}{\mathrm{d}x}$ **(3)**

   ....

   (b) $\dfrac{\mathrm{d}^2y}{\mathrm{d}x^2}$ **(1)**

   > Differentiate twice to find the second-order derivative $\dfrac{\mathrm{d}^2y}{\mathrm{d}x^2}$ (or $f''(x)$).

   ....

> **Guided**

2. The curve C has equation $y = 5x - \dfrac{2}{x^2}$, $x \neq 0$

   The point P has coordinates $(1, 3)$.

   (a) Show that P lies on C. **(1)**

   ....

   ....

   (b) Find the gradient of the curve at P. **(2)**

   $y = 5x - \dfrac{2}{x^2} = 5x - 2x^{\cdots\cdots}$

   $\dfrac{dy}{dx} =$ ....

   > $\dfrac{dy}{dx}$ represents the gradient of the curve C at any point. To find the gradient at P, substitute $x = 1$.

   When $x = 1$, $\dfrac{dy}{dx} =$ ....

   Gradient at $P =$ ....

3. $y = 2x^3 - 4\sqrt{x}$, $x > 0$

   (a) Differentiate to find $\dfrac{\mathrm{d}y}{\mathrm{d}x}$ **(2)**

   ....

   ....

   (b) Find the value of $\dfrac{\mathrm{d}y}{\mathrm{d}x}$ when $x = 2$, giving your answer in the form $a + b\sqrt{2}$ **(2)**

   ....

   ....

   ....

4. $f(x) = 3x - \dfrac{4}{x}$

   (a) Find $f'(x)$. **(2)**

   ....

   Given that $f'(x) = 12$

   (b) find the possible values of x. **(3)**

   ....

   ....

   ....

Tangents and normals

> **Guided**

1. The curve C has equation $y = \frac{1}{3}x^3 + 2x^2 - 8x + 4$

   The point P with coordinates $(3, 7)$ lies on C. Find an equation of the tangent to C at P, giving your answer in the form $y = mx + c$, where m and c are constants. **(5)**

   > The gradient of a curve at any point is the same as the gradient of the tangent to the curve at that point.

   $y = \frac{1}{3}x^3 + 2x^2 - 8x + 4$

   $\frac{dy}{dx} = $ ....

   When $x = 3$, $\frac{dy}{dx} = $ ....

   > Find the value of $\frac{dy}{dx}$ at P, then use $y - y_1 = m(x - x_1)$ to find the equation of the tangent.

   Equation of tangent: $y - $ .... $= $ ....$(x - $ ....$)$

   ....

> **Guided**

2. The curve C has equation $y = 8x + 2x^{\frac{3}{2}} - 3x^2$, $x > 0$

   (a) Show that the point $P(4, 0)$ lies on C. **(1)**

   ....

   (b) Find an expression for $\frac{dy}{dx}$ **(3)**

   ....

   (c) Find an equation of the normal to C at the point P, giving your answer in the form $ax + by + c = 0$, where a, b and c are integers. **(6)**

   > The normal to the curve at P is a straight line that is perpendicular to the tangent.

   $\frac{dy}{dx} = $ ....

   When $x = 4$, $\frac{dy}{dx} = $ ....

   Gradient of tangent $= $ .... so gradient of normal $= $ ....

   > Write the gradient of the tangent as a fraction. Find the gradient of the normal by turning the fraction upside down and changing the sign.

   Equation of normal: $y - $ .... $= $ ....$(x - $ ....$)$

   ....

3. The curve C has equation $y = (x + 2)(x^2 - 9)$

   (a) Show that $\frac{dy}{dx} = 3x^2 + 4x - 9$ **(3)**

   ....

   ....

   (b) Show that $y = 6x + 18$ is an equation of the tangent to C at the point $(-3, 0)$. **(2)**

   ....

   ....

   ....

   The tangent to C at the point R is parallel to the tangent at the point $(-3, 0)$.

   (c) Find the exact x-coordinate of R. **(3)**

   ....

   ....

Integration

> **Guided** 1. Given that $y = 4x - \dfrac{3}{x^2}$, $x \neq 0$, find $\int y \, dx$ **(3)**

$y = 4x - 3x^{-2}$

$\int y \, dx = \dfrac{4x \cdots}{}$ ....

....

....

> **Guided** 2. Find $\int (3x^2 - 5 + x^{-\frac{1}{2}}) \, dx$, giving each term in its simplest form. **(4)**

> Dividing by $\dfrac{a}{b}$ is the same as multiplying by $\dfrac{b}{a}$

$\int (3x^2 - 5 + x^{-\frac{1}{2}}) \, dx = \dfrac{3x^3}{} - $ ....

....

....

....

3. Find $\int \dfrac{6x - 3}{2x^3} \, dx$ **(4)**

....

....

....

....

4. (a) Show that $(3 - 2\sqrt{x})^2$ can be written in the form $9 - k\sqrt{x} + 4x$, where k is a constant to be found. **(2)**

....

....

(b) Find $\int (3 - 2\sqrt{x})^2 \, dx$ **(3)**

....

....

....

5. Given that $\dfrac{4x^2 - 2x^{\frac{5}{2}}}{\sqrt{x}}$ can be written in the form $4x^p - 2x^q$

(a) write down the value of p and the value of q. **(2)**

....

....

(b) Find $\int \dfrac{4x^2 - 2x^{\frac{5}{2}}}{\sqrt{x}} \, dx$ **(3)**

....

....

....

....

Finding the constant

> **Guided**

1. The curve C with equation $y = f(x)$, $x \neq 0$, passes through the point (2, 10).

Given that $f'(x) = 3x + \dfrac{2}{x^2}$

(a) find $f(x)$ **(5)**

> To find $f(x)$ you need to integrate $f'(x)$.

> To find the constant of integration, use $f(x) = 10$ when $x = 2$.

$f(x) = \int\left(3x + \dfrac{2}{x^2}\right) dx$

     $= \int(3x + 2x^{\cdots\cdots}) \, dx$

     $= \text{.....................} + c$

     $= \text{..}$

$10 = \text{.....................} + c$

$c = \text{............}$

$f(x) = \text{..}$

(b) verify that $f(-1) = 8.5$ **(1)**

> To find $f(-1)$ substitute $x = -1$ into the equation for $f(x)$.

$f(x) = \text{..}$

$f(-1) = \text{..} = \text{............}$

> **Guided**

2. The gradient of a curve C is given by $\dfrac{dy}{dx} = \dfrac{x-3}{\sqrt{x}}$, $x \neq 0$

The point $(4, \frac{1}{3})$ lies on C. Find y in terms of x.   **(6)**

> To find y you need to integrate $\dfrac{dy}{dx}$

$\dfrac{dy}{dx} = \dfrac{x-3}{\sqrt{x}} = x^{\cdots\cdots} - 3x^{\cdots\cdots}$

$y = \int(x^{\cdots\cdots} - 3x^{\cdots\cdots}) \, dx = \text{.....................} + c$

> To find the constant of integration, use $y = \frac{1}{3}$ when $x = 4$.

$\dfrac{1}{3} = \text{..} + c$

     $= \text{.....................}$

$c = \text{.....................}$

$y = \text{..}$

3. The gradient of a curve C is given by $\dfrac{dy}{dx} = \dfrac{(x^2 - 2)^2}{x^2}$, $x \neq 0$

(a) Show that $\dfrac{dy}{dx} = x^2 - 4 + 4x^{-2}$ **(2)**

....

....

The point $(3, \frac{2}{3})$ lies on C.

(b) Find an equation for the curve C in the form $y = f(x)$.   **(6)**

....

....

....

....

....

....

You are the examiner!

Checking through your work is a key skill for AS maths. Have a look at pages 26 and 27 of the *Revision Guide*, then practise with these questions. There are full worked solutions on page 162.

1. Express $\dfrac{4 + 2\sqrt{5}}{3 + \sqrt{5}}$ in the form $a + b\sqrt{5}$, where a and b are rational numbers. **(4)**

....

....

....

....

....

....

....

> Be really careful with your algebra. If you have to multiply a fraction by an expression, use **brackets** to make sure you multiply **every term**.

2. The equation $x^2 - 4px + 2p = 0$, where p is a non-zero constant, has equal roots. Find the value of p. **(4)**

....

....

....

....

....

....

....

> Use **brackets** when you are substituting **negative numbers** into any formula. And be especially careful when dealing with **squares** or **fractions**.

3. Find $\displaystyle\int\left(6x^2 - \frac{4}{x^2} + 3\sqrt{x}\right)dx$, giving each term in its simplest form. **(4)**

....

....

....

....

....

....

....

....

> Write every term in the polynomial in the form ax^n before integrating.

> Dividing by $\frac{a}{b}$ is the same as multiplying by $\frac{b}{a}$

> If you are doing **indefinite** integration you may lose a mark if you forget the **constant of integration**.

You are the examiner!

> Checking through your work is a key skill for AS maths. Have a look at pages 26 and 27 of the *Revision Guide*, then practise with these questions. There are full worked solutions on page 162.

4. Find the set of values of x for which

    (a) $3(x - 5) > 6 - 4x$ **(2)**

    ....

    ....

    ....

    (b) $x(x - 3) > 10$ **(4)**

    ....

    ....

    ....

    > If you are solving a quadratic inequality, always **draw a sketch** to identify the correct set of values.

    ....

    ....

    ....

    (c) **both** $3(x - 5) > 6 - 4x$ **and** $x(x - 3) > 10$ **(1)**

    ....

    > Show both sets of solutions on a number line. The values where the inequalities **overlap** are the values which satisfy them both.

    ....

    ....

    ....

5. On separate diagrams, sketch the graph of

    (a) $y = (x - 2)^2$ **(3)**

    (b) $y = (x - 2)^2 + k$ **(2)**

    Show on each sketch the coordinates of each point at which the graph meets the axes.

    > **Read the question** carefully and make sure you are giving all the information asked for. When sketching a graph, you should label the points of intersection with **both** axes.

    ....

    ....

The factor theorem

> **Guided**

1. (a) Use the factor theorem to show that $(x + 2)$ is a factor of $2x^3 - 3x^2 - 11x + 6$ **(2)**

$f(x) = 2x^3 - 3x^2 - 11x + 6$

$f(\underline{\quad}) = 2(\underline{\quad})^3 - 3(\underline{\quad})^2 - 11(\underline{\quad}) + 6$

$= \text{..}$

$= \text{................}$

So $(x + 2)$ is a $\text{.........................}$

> If $(x + 2)$ is a factor then $f(-2) = 0$.

> Remember to write a conclusion or begin by stating, 'If $(x + 2)$ is a factor then $f(-2) = 0$.'

(b) Factorise $2x^3 - 3x^2 - 11x + 6$ completely.   **(4)**

$f(x) = (x + 2)(2x^2 \text{..............................})$

$= (x + 2)(2x\text{................})(\text{................})$

> One method to factorise the polynomial is by using synthetic division.
>
> | -2 | 2 | -3 | -11 | 6 |
> |---|---|---|---|---|
> | | | | -4 | |
> | | 2 | -7 | | |

2. $f(x) = 2x^3 - x^2 - 22x + c$, where c is a constant.
Given that $f(4) = 0$

(a) find the value of c **(2)**

(b) factorise $f(x)$ completely.   **(4)**

3. $f(x) = 2x^3 + 3x^2 - 39x - 20$
Given that $(x + 5)$ is a factor of $f(x)$, find all the solutions of $f(x) = 0$ **(5)**

The remainder theorem

Guided   **1.** Find the remainder when $2x^3 + 3x^2 - 7x - 2$ is divided by

(i) $x + 3$

f$(x) = 2x^3 + 3x^2 - 7x - 2$

> To find the remainder work out f(−3).

f$(-3) = 2(\underline{\quad})^3 + 3(\underline{\quad})^2 - 7(\underline{\quad}) - 2$

    $= \dots\dots\dots\dots\dots\dots\dots\dots\dots\dots\dots\dots$

remainder is $\dots\dots\dots\dots\dots\dots\dots\dots\dots\dots\dots\dots$

(ii) $2x - 1$ **(3)**

f$(\underline{\quad}) = 2(\underline{\quad})^3 + 3(\underline{\quad})^2 - 7(\underline{\quad}) - 2$

> To find the value of x to substitute into f(x), solve $2x - 1 = 0$.

    $= \dots\dots\dots\dots\dots\dots\dots\dots\dots\dots\dots\dots$

$\dots\dots\dots\dots\dots\dots\dots\dots\dots\dots\dots\dots$

Guided   **2.** f$(x) = 2x^3 + ax^2 + bx + 3$, where a and b are constants.
Given that, when f(x) is divided by $(x - 2)$ the remainder is 27,
(a) show that $2a + b = 4$ **(2)**

f$(2) = 2(\underline{\quad})^3 + a(\underline{\quad})^2 + b(\underline{\quad}) + 3 = 27$

> Work out f(2) in terms of a and b, equate to 27 and then simplify.

$\dots\dots\dots\dots\dots\dots\dots\dots\dots\dots = 27$

$\dots\dots\dots\dots\dots\dots\dots\dots\dots\dots\dots\dots\dots\dots\dots\dots\dots\dots\dots\dots\dots\dots\dots$

$\dots\dots\dots\dots\dots\dots\dots\dots\dots\dots\dots\dots\dots\dots\dots\dots\dots\dots\dots\dots\dots\dots\dots$

Given also that when f(x) is divided by $(x + 1)$ the remainder is 12,
(b) find the value of a and the value of b.   **(4)**

f$(-1) = 2(\underline{\quad})^3 + a(\underline{\quad})^2 + b(\underline{\quad}) + 3 = 12$

> Work out f(−1) in terms of a and b and equate to 12, then solve the two equations simultaneously.

$\dots\dots\dots\dots\dots\dots\dots\dots\dots\dots = 12$

$\dots\dots\dots\dots\dots\dots\dots\dots\dots\dots\dots\dots\dots\dots\dots\dots\dots\dots\dots\dots\dots\dots\dots$

$\dots\dots\dots\dots\dots\dots\dots\dots\dots\dots\dots\dots\dots\dots\dots\dots\dots\dots\dots\dots\dots\dots\dots$

$\dots\dots\dots\dots\dots\dots\dots\dots\dots\dots\dots\dots\dots\dots\dots\dots\dots\dots\dots\dots\dots\dots\dots$

$\dots\dots\dots\dots\dots\dots\dots\dots\dots\dots\dots\dots\dots\dots\dots\dots\dots\dots\dots\dots\dots\dots\dots$

3. f$(x) = ax^3 - 5x^2 + bx - 4$, where a and b are constants.
When f(x) is divided by $(x + 2)$ the remainder is -62
When f(x) is divided by $(x - 1)$ the remainder is 1
Find the value of a and the value of b.   **(5)**

$\dots\dots\dots\dots\dots\dots\dots\dots\dots\dots\dots\dots\dots\dots\dots\dots\dots\dots\dots\dots\dots\dots\dots$

$\dots\dots\dots\dots\dots\dots\dots\dots\dots\dots\dots\dots\dots\dots\dots\dots\dots\dots\dots\dots\dots\dots\dots$

$\dots\dots\dots\dots\dots\dots\dots\dots\dots\dots\dots\dots\dots\dots\dots\dots\dots\dots\dots\dots\dots\dots\dots$

$\dots\dots\dots\dots\dots\dots\dots\dots\dots\dots\dots\dots\dots\dots\dots\dots\dots\dots\dots\dots\dots\dots\dots$

$\dots\dots\dots\dots\dots\dots\dots\dots\dots\dots\dots\dots\dots\dots\dots\dots\dots\dots\dots\dots\dots\dots\dots$

$\dots\dots\dots\dots\dots\dots\dots\dots\dots\dots\dots\dots\dots\dots\dots\dots\dots\dots\dots\dots\dots\dots\dots$

Equation of a circle

1. A circle C has centre $(4, -1)$ and radius 6
   Write down the equation of the circle in the form $(x - a)^2 + (y - b)^2 = r^2$ **(2)**

   ....

> **Guided**

2. The circle C has centre $(2, 3)$ and passes through the point $(-1, 7)$.

   (a) Find an equation for C.   **(4)**

   $r = \sqrt{(-1 - 2)^2 + (\ldots - \ldots)^2} = \ldots$

   $(x \ldots)^2 + (y \ldots)^2 = r^2$

   ....

   | First find r^2 using the formula for the distance between two points. |

   | Then find an equation of C using $(x - a)^2 + (y - b)^2 = r^2$ where (a, b) are the coordinates of the centre of C. |

   (b) Verify that the point $(5, 7)$ lies on C.   **(1)**

   $(5 \ldots)^2 + (7 \ldots)^2 = $ ....

   ....

   ....

   | Substitute $x = 5$ (and $y = 7$) into the left-hand side of the equation of the circle. Show all your working to verify that the expression is equal to $25 = 5^2$. |

   ....

> **Guided**

3. The circle C has equation $x^2 + y^2 + 2x - 6y = 6$

   (a) Find the centre and the radius of C.   **(5)**

   $x^2 + 2x + y^2 - 6y = 6$

   $(x \ldots)^2 - \ldots + (y \ldots)^2 - \ldots = 6$

   | First rearrange the formula, then complete the square to write it in the form $(x - a)^2 + (y - b)^2 = r^2$. |

   ....

   (b) Find the coordinates of the points where C crosses the x-axis, giving your answers as simplified surds.   **(4)**

   | Substitute $y = 0$ into your equation and rearrange to find the corresponding x-values in surd form. |

   ....

   ....

   ....

   ....

   ....

4. The points A and B have coordinates $(-3, 5)$ and $(5, 11)$ respectively.
   Given that AB is a diameter of the circle C, find an equation for C.   **(5)**

   ....

   ....

   ....

   ....

Circle properties

1. The circle C has equation $x^2 + y^2 + 4x - 6y = 12$
    The points $P(1, 7)$ and $Q(-5, -1)$ lie on the circle. Show that PQ is a diameter of C. **(2)**

    ....

    ....

    ....

Guided 2. The line $5y = 3x + 32$ is a tangent to the circle C, touching C at the point $P(1, 7)$, as shown in the diagram. The point Q is the centre of C.

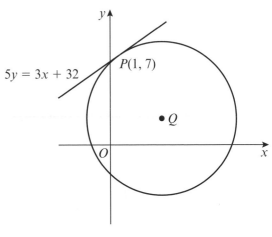

(a) Find an equation of the straight line through P and Q in the form $ax + by + c = 0$, where a, b and c are integers. **(3)**

> The line through P and Q is **perpendicular** to the tangent.

> To find the equation of the line use $y - y_1 = m(x - x_1)$.

Gradient of tangent = ...

Gradient of line through P and Q = ...

Equation of line is $y - y_1 = m(x - x_1)$

....

....

(b) Given that Q lies on the line $y = 2$, find the coordinates of Q. **(1)**

....

....

3. The points $P(3, -1)$, $Q(4, 4)$ and $R(a, 3)$ lie on the circle C, as shown in the diagram.
    Given that PR is a diameter of C, find the value of a. **(3)**

> Triangle PQR is right angled so PQ is perpendicular to QR.

....

....

....

....

....

....

....

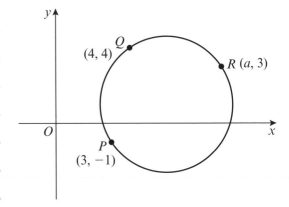

Geometric sequences

1. A geometric sequence has first term $a = 640$ and common ratio $r = \frac{5}{8}$
    Find the 15th term of the sequence, giving your answer to 3 significant figures.   **(2)**

    ....

    > The nth term of a geometric sequence is $u_n = ar^{n-1}$.

    ....

Guided 2. The fourth term of a geometric sequence is 72 and the seventh term of the series is 9
    For this sequence, find

    (a) the common ratio   **(2)**

    > Divide ② by ① to eliminate a and find r. Note that, as terms are getting smaller, r must be less than 1.

    Fourth term: $ar^{\cdots} = 72$ ①

    Seventh term: $ar^{\cdots} = 9$ ②

    ② ÷ ①: ....

    ....

    (b) the first term.   **(2)**

    > Substitute your value of r into ① or ② to work out the value of a.

    ....

Guided 3. The first three terms of a geometric sequence are k, 15 and $k + 40$ respectively.
    Find two possible values of k.   **(5)**

    > The common ratio is found by dividing any term of the sequence by the previous term.

    > Rearrange to find a quadratic equation and solve by factorising.

    $\dfrac{15}{k} = \dfrac{\cdots\cdots}{\cdots\cdots}$

    ....

    ....

    ....

4. The first three terms of a geometric sequence are $(k + 6)$, k and $(2k - 16)$ respectively, where k is a positive constant.

    (a) Show that $k^2 - 4k - 96 = 0$ **(4)**

    ....

    ....

    ....

    ....

    (b) Hence show that $k = 12$ **(2)**

    ....

    ....

    (c) Find the common ratio of this sequence.   **(2)**

    ....

    ....

Geometric series

Guided 1. A geometric series has first term 150 and common ratio $\frac{2}{3}$
Find the sum of the first 20 terms of the series, giving your answer to 1 decimal place. **(2)**

$$S_{20} = \frac{150(1 - (\ldots\ldots)^{\ldots\ldots})}{1 - (\ldots\ldots)} = \ldots\ldots\ldots\ldots\ldots$$

> The sum of the first n terms is $S_n = \frac{a(1 - r^n)}{1 - r}$

....

....

Guided 2. Find $\displaystyle\sum_{k=1}^{8} 10(3^k)$ **(3)**

> Write out some of the terms of the sequence to help you work out the values of a and r.

$$\sum_{k=1}^{8} 10(3^k) = 30 + \ldots\ldots + \ldots\ldots + \ldots\ldots + \ldots$$

$$a = \ldots\ldots \qquad r = \ldots\ldots$$

$$S_8 = \frac{\ldots\ldots(\ldots\ldots\ldots\ldots\ldots)}{\ldots\ldots\ldots\ldots\ldots\ldots} = \ldots\ldots\ldots\ldots = \ldots\ldots\ldots$$

3. A geometric series has first term 8 and common ratio -1.2
Find the sum of the first 50 terms of the series, giving your answer to 1 decimal place. **(2)**

....

....

....

4. In the geometric series $1 + 3 + 9 + 27 + \ldots$, each term is 3 times the previous term.
Find the sum of the first n terms of this series. **(4)**

....

....

....

5. Ms Burton will receive a salary of £38 000 in 2014. Each year she will receive an increase in salary of 3% so that her annual salaries form a geometric sequence. The first increase in salary is given in 2015.

(a) Find, to the nearest £100, Ms Burton's salary in the year 2017. **(2)**

....

....

(b) Find, to the nearest £1000, the total amount of salary she will receive from 2014 until 2026. **(4)**

....

....

....

Infinite series

Guided   **1.** Find the sum to infinity of the geometric series $\frac{2}{3} + \frac{1}{2} + \frac{3}{8} + \dots$ **(3)**

$a = \dots\dots\dots\dots$ $r = \dfrac{\frac{1}{2}}{\dfrac{\dots\dots}{\dots\dots}} \div = \dots\dots\dots\dots$

> Find r by working out $u_2 \div u_1$.
> You can check your answer by working out $u_3 \div u_2$.

$S_\infty = \dfrac{a}{1 - r} = \dfrac{\dots\dots}{1 - \dots\dots} = \dots\dots\dots\dots$

> $S_\infty = \dfrac{a}{1 - r}$, provided $-1 < r < 1$.

Guided   **2.** The first term of a geometric series is 150 and the sum to infinity of the series is 375
Find the common ratio.   **(3)**

$a = \dots\dots\dots\dots$ $S_\infty = \dfrac{a}{1 - r} = \dfrac{\dots\dots\dots\dots}{1 - \dots\dots\dots\dots} = 375$ > Rearrange the equation for S_∞ to find r.

3. The first three terms of a geometric series are 15, 13.5 and 12.15 respectively.

(a) Find the sum to infinity of the geometric series.   **(3)**

(b) State the condition for an infinite geometric series with common ratio r to be convergent.   **(1)**

(c) Find the difference between the sum to infinity of this series and the sum of the first 50 terms, giving your answer to 3 decimal places.   **(3)**

4. A geometric series has first term a and common ratio r. The second term of the series is 12 and the sum to infinity of the series is 50

(a) Show that $25r^2 - 25r + 6 = 0$ **(4)**

(b) Find the two possible values of r and the corresponding values of a.   **(4)**

Binomial expansion

> **Guided**

1. Find the first 3 terms, in ascending powers of x, of the binomial expansion of $(3 - 2x)^5$, giving each term in its simplest form. **(4)**

    The expansion for $(a + b)^n$ is
    $$a^n + \binom{n}{1}a^{n-1}b + \binom{n}{2}a^{n-2}b^2 + \dots + b^n$$
    where $\binom{n}{r} = \dfrac{n!}{r!(n-r)!}$

    $a =$ .... $b =$ .... $n =$ ....

    $(3 - 2x)^5 = (3)^5 + \binom{5}{1}(3)^4(\text{..........}) +$ ....

    $=$ ....

    ....

    Remember to use brackets when substituting and be careful when substituting negative numbers.

> **Guided**

2. (a) Write down the first 3 terms, in ascending powers of x, of the binomial expansion of $(1 + px)^9$, where p is a non-zero constant. **(2)**

    $a =$ .... $b =$ .... $n =$ ....

    Remember that $1^n = 1$.

    $(1 + px)^9 = 1^9 +$ ....

    $=$ ....

    (b) Given that, in the expansion of $(1 + px)^9$, the coefficient of x is q and the coefficient of x^2 is $20q$, find the value of p and the value of q. **(4)**

    $(1 + px)^9 =$ ....

    .... $= q$ .... $= 20q$

    Solve the equations simultaneously to find the values of p and q.

    ....

    ....

3. Find the first 3 terms, in ascending powers of x, of the binomial expansion of $(4 - 3x)^7$ and simplify each term. **(4)**

    ....

    ....

    ....

4. (a) Find the first 3 terms, in ascending powers of x, of the binomial expansion of $(2 + kx)^6$, where k is a constant. Give each term in its simplest form. **(4)**

    ....

    ....

    ....

    (b) Given that, in the expansion of $(2 + kx)^6$, the coefficient of x is $4q$ and the coefficient of x^2 is $25q$, find the value of k and the value of q. **(2)**

    ....

    ....

    ....

    ....

Solving binomial problems

> **Guided** 1. Find the coefficient of x^7 in the expansion of $\left(4 - \frac{x}{2}\right)^{12}$ (2)

> Use the formula for the general term given in the formulae booklet: $\binom{n}{r}a^{n-r}b^r$.

$n = \text{............}$ $r = \text{............}$ $a = \text{............}$ $b = \text{............}$

$\binom{12}{\text{......}} 4^{\text{......}} \left(-\frac{x}{2}\right)^{\text{......}} = \text{..}$

....

Coefficient = ...

> **Guided** 2. The first 4 terms of the expansion of $\left(1 + \frac{x}{2}\right)^8$ are given below:

> Find the value of x to substitute in by solving $1 + \frac{x}{2} = 1.005$.

$$\left(1 + \frac{x}{2}\right)^8 = 1 + 4x + 7x^2 + 7x^3 + \ldots$$

Use the expansion to estimate the value of $(1.005)^8$, giving your answer to 5 decimal places. (2)

$1 + \frac{x}{2} = 1.005$

$x = \text{............}$

$(1.005)^8 \approx 1 + 4(\text{............}) + 7(\text{............})^2 + 7(\text{............})^3$

....

3. (a) Find the first 4 terms of the binomial expansion, in ascending powers of x, of $\left(1 + \frac{x}{4}\right)^9$, giving each term in its simplest form. (4)

....

....

....

....

(b) Use your expansion to estimate the value of $(1.025)^9$, giving your answer to 4 decimal places. (3)

....

....

....

4. (a) Find the first 4 terms, in ascending powers of x, of the binomial expansion of $(1 - 2x)^7$ Give each term in its simplest form. (4)

....

....

....

(b) If x is small, so that x^2 and higher powers can be ignored, show that
$(1 + x)(1 - 2x)^7 \approx 1 - 13x$ (2)

....

....

Radians, arcs and sectors

Guided   1. In the diagram, OAB is a sector of a circle, radius 6 cm.
The arc AB is 9 cm long.
Find

(a) the size of $\angle AOB$ in radians   **(2)**

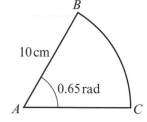

> Use arc length $= r\theta$ to work out the size of $\angle AOB$.

$$9 = \text{...........} \, \theta \qquad \theta = \text{.......................}$$

(b) the area of the sector AOB.   **(2)**

$$\text{Area} = \frac{1}{2}r^2\theta = \frac{1}{2} \times \text{...........}^2 \times \text{...........} = \text{...........} \, cm^2$$

> Use area $= \frac{1}{2}r^2\theta$ to work out the area of the sector.

Guided   2. In the diagram, ABC is a sector of a circle, radius 10 cm.
Given that the size of $\angle BAC$ is 0.65 radians, find

(a) the perimeter of the sector ABC **(3)**

> Perimeter = arc length + 2 × radius

$$\text{Arc length} = r\theta = \text{.................} = \text{...........} \, cm$$

$$\text{Perimeter} = \text{...........} + \text{...........} + \text{...........} = \text{...........} \, cm$$

(b) the area of the sector.   **(2)**

$$\text{Area} = \frac{1}{2}r^2\theta = \frac{1}{2} \times \text{.................} = \text{...........} \, cm^2$$

3. In the diagram, PQR is a sector of a circle, radius 7 cm
and angle $PQR = \dfrac{2\pi}{3}$
Find

(a) the exact length of arc PR **(2)**

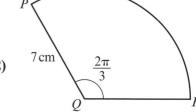

> Watch for questions which ask for **exact** answers. This usually means giving your answer in terms of π or in surd form.

....

(b) the exact value of the area of the sector.   **(2)**

....

4. In the diagram, AOB is a sector of a circle radius 8 cm.
The area of the sector is 45 cm².
Find

(a) the size of $\angle AOB$ in radians to 3 significant figures   **(3)**

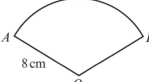

....

....

(b) the perimeter of sector AOB.   **(3)**

....

....

Cosine rule

Guided   1.   In the triangle ABC, $AB = 8$ cm, $AC = 5$ cm
and $\angle BAC = 2.1$ radians.
Find the length of BC to 3 significant figures.   **(3)**

Sketch the triangle and label the sides a, b and c. You know two sides and the angle between them, so use the cosine rule.

The angle is given in radians so make sure your calculator is in radians mode.

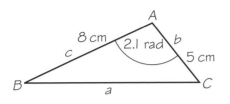

$a^2 = b^2 + c^2 - 2bc\cos A$

$a^2 = 5^2 + \text{............}^2 - 2 \times \text{............} \times \text{............} \times \cos 2.1 = \text{.........................}$

$a = \text{............}$ cm

Guided   2.   In the triangle ABC, $AB = 6$ cm, $AC = 12$ cm and
$BC = 9$ cm. Find the size of angle B, giving your answer
in radians to 3 significant figures.   **(3)**

Sketch the triangle and label the sides a, b and c. You know all three sides so use the cosine rule.

$\cos B = \dfrac{a^2 + c^2 - b^2}{2ac}$

$= \dfrac{9^2 + \text{.....}^2 - \text{.....}^2}{2 \times \text{.....} \times \text{.....}} = \text{............}$

$B = \cos^{-1}(\text{............}) = \text{.........................}$

3.   In the triangle ABC, $AB = 4$ cm, $BC = 6$ cm and $CA = 8$ cm.

(a) Show that $\cos A = \dfrac{11}{16}$ **(3)**

....

....

(b) Hence, or otherwise, find the exact value
of $\sin A$.   **(2)**

Use Pythagoras to find the exact value of $\sin A$.

....

....

....

....

4.   The diagram shows a lighthouse at O and two boats, one at
P and one at Q. Boat P is 600 m due north of the lighthouse
at O and boat Q is 900 m from O. The bearing of Q from O
is 025°. Calculate the distance between boat P and
boat Q, in metres, to 3 significant figures.   **(3)**

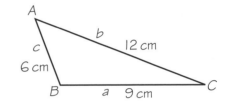

....

....

....

....

Sine rule

Guided **1.** In the triangle ABC, $AC = 9$ cm, $\angle BAC = 0.9$ radians
and $\angle ACB = 1.1$ radians.
Find the length of AB to 3 significant figures. **(3)**

$\angle ABC = \pi - 0.9 - 1.1 = \ldots\ldots\ldots$

$$\frac{b}{\sin B} = \frac{c}{\sin C}$$

$$\frac{\ldots\ldots}{\sin \ldots\ldots} = \frac{c}{\sin \ldots\ldots}$$

so $c = \dfrac{\ldots\ldots \sin \ldots\ldots}{\sin \ldots\ldots} = \ldots\ldots$ cm (3 s.f.)

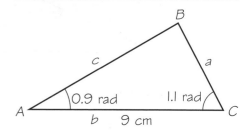

Not SAS or SSS so use the sine rule.

First find angle B using the fact that
angles in a triangle add up to π radians.

Guided **2.** In the triangle PQR, $PQ = 14$ cm, $PR = 8$ cm,
$\angle PQR = 0.3$ radians and $\angle PRQ = x$ radians.

(a) Use the sine rule to find the value of $\sin x$,
giving your answer to 3 decimal places. **(3)**

$$\frac{\sin x}{\ldots\ldots} = \frac{\sin \ldots\ldots}{\ldots\ldots} \qquad \sin x = \frac{\ldots\ldots \sin \ldots\ldots}{\ldots\ldots} = \ldots\ldots$$

If it helps, you can re-label the
triangle ABC instead of PQR.

Use the alternative form of the sine
rule when working out an angle.

(b) Given that there are two possible values of x, find these
values of x, giving your answers to 2 decimal places. **(3)**

Use $\sin x = \sin(\pi - x)$.

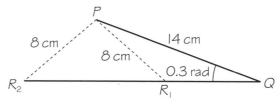

$x = \sin^{-1}(\ldots\ldots) = \ldots\ldots$ or $x = \pi - (\ldots\ldots) = \ldots\ldots$

3. In the triangle ABC, $AC = 15$ cm, $\angle ABC = \frac{\pi}{6}$ and $\angle ACB = \frac{\pi}{4}$. Find the length of BC. **(3)**

....

....

....

....

....

4. In the triangle ABC, $AB = 3.7$ cm, $AC = 5.4$ cm and $\angle ABC = 120°$.
Find the size of $\angle ACB$ in degrees to the nearest degree. **(3)**

....

....

....

....

....

Areas of triangles

Guided 1. In the diagram, $PQRS$ is a sector of a circle with centre Q and radius $5\sqrt{2}$ cm.
Given that the length of the straight line PR is 10 cm,

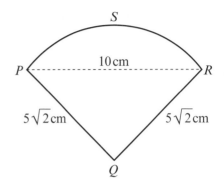

(a) find the exact size of angle PQR in radians. **(3)**

$$\cos Q = \frac{PQ^2 + QR^2 - PR^2}{2 \times PQ \times QR}$$

$$= \frac{(........)^2 + (........)^2 - (........)^2}{2 \times .... \times ....}$$

$$= \frac{\overline{.............\ ....}}{.............} = ...$$

$Q = ...$

(b) Show that the area of $PQRS$ is $\frac{25}{2}\pi$ cm². **(2)**

Area of sector $= \frac{1}{2}r^2\theta = \frac{1}{2} \times$ .... $=$ ....

Area $=$ .... cm²

(c) Find the exact area of the triangle PQR. **(2)**

Area of triangle $= \frac{1}{2}ab\sin\theta$

$$= \frac{1}{2} \times \text{.....................................} = \text{............}$$

Area $=$ .... cm²

> When you know two sides and the included angle of a triangle you can use: Area $= \frac{1}{2} ab \sin \theta$

Guided 2. In the diagram, ABC is a triangle and ABD is a sector of a circle with centre A. Find the shaded area, R, giving your answer to 3 significant figures. **(5)**

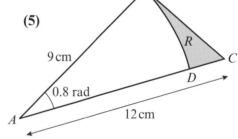

> Area of R = area of triangle ABC – area of sector ABD

Area of $ABC =$ ....

Area of $ABD =$ ....

Area of $R =$ ....

3. The diagram shows ABC, a sector of a circle with centre A and radius 7 cm. The size of $\angle BAC$ is 0.8 radians and D is the midpoint of AC. Find the area of R, giving your answer to 3 significant figures. **(6)**

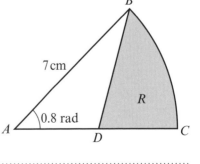

....

....

....

....

....

Trigonometric graphs

1. (a) Sketch, for $0 \leqslant x \leqslant 2\pi$, the graph of $y = 3\cos x$ **(2)**

(b) Write down the coordinates of the maximum and minimum points. **(2)**

....

Guided 2. (a) Sketch, for $0 \leqslant x \leqslant 2\pi$, the graph of $y = \sin\left(x - \dfrac{\pi}{3}\right)$ **(2)**

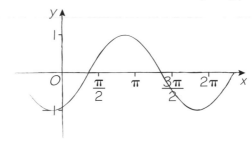

> The graph of $y = \sin\left(x - \dfrac{\pi}{3}\right)$ is a translation of the graph of $y = \sin x$ by $\begin{pmatrix} \frac{\pi}{3} \\ 0 \end{pmatrix}$

(b) Write down the exact coordinates of the points where the graph meets the coordinate axes. **(3)**

> You should know the exact values of sin, cos and tan of $\dfrac{\pi}{6}, \dfrac{\pi}{4}$ and $\dfrac{\pi}{3}$

When $x = 0$: $y = \sin\left(0 - \dfrac{\pi}{3}\right) = -\sin\left(\dfrac{\pi}{3}\right) = \dfrac{\text{.......}}{\text{.......}}$

$\left(0, \dfrac{\text{.......}}{\text{.......}}\right)$

When $y = 0$: $0 = \sin\left(x - \dfrac{\pi}{3}\right)$

so $x = \text{.......} + \dfrac{\pi}{3} = \text{.............}$ or $x = \text{.............}$

$(\text{......}, 0)$ and $(\text{......}, 0)$

3. The diagram shows part of the curve with equation $y = \cos(ax + b)$, where $a > 0$ and $0 < b < \pi$

The curve cuts the x-axis at the points P, Q and R as shown.

Given that the coordinates of P, Q and R are $\left(\dfrac{\pi}{8}, 0\right)$, $\left(\dfrac{5\pi}{8}, 0\right)$ and $\left(\dfrac{9\pi}{8}, 0\right)$ respectively,

find the values of a and b. **(4)**

> The graph of $y = \cos x$ crosses the x-axis at $\dfrac{\pi}{2}, \dfrac{3\pi}{2}$, etc.

> Write down two equations and solve them simultaneously to find a and b.

....

....

....

....

....

Trigonometric equations 1

Guided 1. Solve $5 \sin x = 2$ in the interval $0 \leq x \leq 2\pi$, giving your answers to 3 decimal places. **(3)**

> Draw a sketch of $y = \sin x$ for the range given in the question. This will tell you the number of solutions there are within the range.

> Check your calculator is in radians mode and work out $\sin^{-1}\left(\frac{2}{5}\right)$ to find the **principal value** of x.

> To find the second value of x, work out $\pi - $ (principal value).

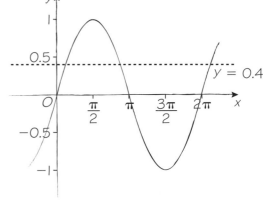

$\sin x = \dfrac{2}{5} = 0.4$

$x = \sin^{-1}(0.4) = $ .... or $x = \pi - $ .... $ = $ ....

Guided 2. Solve $\tan x = 3$ in the interval $0 \leq x \leq 360°$, giving your answers to 1 decimal place. **(3)**

$\tan x = 3$

$x = \tan^{-1}(3) = $ ....

or $x = 180° + $ ....

> You can use a CAST diagram to answer this question.

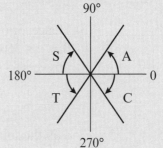

3. (a) Sketch the graph of $y = \cos x$ in the interval $0 \leq x \leq 2\pi$ **(2)**

(b) Find the values of x in the interval $0 \leq x \leq 2\pi$ for which $\cos x = -0.2$, giving your answers correct to 3 decimal places. **(3)**

....

....

4. Solve the following equations in the interval $-180° \leq x \leq 180°$, giving your answers to 1 decimal place.

(a) $5 \sin x + 3 = 0$ **(3)**

....

....

....

(b) $3 \cos x = 2$ **(3)**

....

....

....

Trigonometric identities

> **Guided** 1. (a) Show that the equation $3 \sin x = 2 \cos^2 x$ can be written in the form $2 \sin^2 x + 3 \sin x - 2 = 0$ **(2)**

> Write everything in terms of $\sin^2 x$ and $\sin x$ by using $\sin^2 x + \cos^2 x = 1$.

$3 \sin x = 2 \cos^2 x$ $\qquad$ $\sin^2 x + \cos^2 x = 1$ so $\cos^2 x = $ ....

$3 \sin x = 2($ .... $)$

....

(b) Hence solve, for $0 \leqslant x < 360°$, $3 \sin x = 2 \cos^2 x$ **(4)**

$2 \sin^2 x + 3 \sin x - 2 = 0$

$(2 \sin x$ ....$)(\sin x$ ....$) = 0$

$\sin x = $ ....

$x = $ .... or $\qquad x = $ ....

> Factorise the quadratic to find solutions for $\sin x$. Remember that $-1 \leqslant \sin x \leqslant 1$, so only one of the factors will give you solutions.

> **Guided** 2. (a) Given that $2 \cos \theta = 3 \sin \theta$, find the value of $\tan \theta$.   **(1)**

$\dfrac{\sin \theta}{\cos \theta} = \dfrac{............}{............}$ $\qquad$ $\tan \theta = $ ....

> Rearrange the equation to find $\dfrac{\sin \theta}{\cos \theta} = \tan \theta$.

(b) Hence, or otherwise, find the values of θ in the interval $0 \leqslant \theta < 360°$ for which $2 \cos \theta = 3 \sin \theta$, giving your answers to 1 decimal place.   **(3)**

> Find $\tan^{-1} \theta$. Remember that there are two solutions in the range.

$\theta = \tan^{-1} ($ ....$)$ $\quad \theta = $ .... or $\theta = $ ....

3. Find all the solutions, in the interval $0 \leqslant \theta < 2\pi$, of the equation $(1 - \tan \theta)(2 \sin \theta + 1) = 0$, giving each solution in terms of π **(4)**

....

....

....

....

4. (a) Show that the equation $\cos \theta \tan \theta = 4 \cos^2 \theta + 1$ can be written in the form $4 \sin^2 \theta + \sin \theta - 5 = 0$ **(3)**

....

....

....

....

....

(b) Hence solve, for $0 \leqslant \theta < 360°$, $\cos \theta \tan \theta = 4 \cos^2 \theta + 1$, showing each stage of your working.   **(5)**

....

....

....

....

Trigonometric equations 2

⟩**Guided**⟩

1. Solve, for $0 \leqslant x \leqslant 180°$, the equation

   (a) $\sin 2x = \frac{1}{2}$ **(4)**

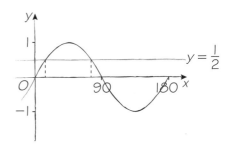

The range for $2x$ is twice the range for x.

You should know $\sin 30° = \cos 60° = \frac{1}{2}$

The sketch shows that there are two solutions of $\sin 2x = \frac{1}{2}$ for $0 \leqslant x \leqslant 180°$.

$0 \leqslant 2x \leqslant$ ....°   Let $Z = 2x$

     $Z = \sin^{-1}\left(\frac{1}{2}\right) =$ ....

or $Z = 180 -$ .... $=$ ....

$2x =$ ....   or   ....

  $x =$ ....   or   ....

   (b) $\cos(x - 50°) = 0.3$, giving your answers to 1 decimal place. **(4)**

.............° $\leqslant x - 50° \leqslant$ ....°   Let $Z = x - 50°$

     $Z = \cos^{-1}(0.3) =$ ....

or $Z = 360 -$ .... $=$ ....

$x - 50° =$ ....

     $x =$ ....

Check that your solutions for x lie within the given range.

2. Solve, for $-\pi \leqslant x < \pi$, $\tan\left(x + \frac{\pi}{4}\right) = 2.5$, giving your answers to 3 decimal places. **(3)**

....

....

....

....

3. (a) Find all the values of θ, to 1 decimal place, in the interval $0° \leqslant \theta < 360°$ for which
   $4\sin(\theta + 10°) = 3$ **(4)**

....

....

....

   (b) Find the exact values of θ in the interval $0° \leqslant \theta < 360°$ for which $\tan^2 \theta = 3$ **(5)**

....

....

....

....

....

Logarithms

> **Guided**   1.   (i) Write down the value of $\log_8 64$ (1)

$8^{\cdots} = 64$ so $\log_8 64 = \ldots\ldots$

(ii) Express $3\log_a 2 + \log_a 7$ as a single logarithm to base a.   (3)

$3\log_a 2 = \log_a 2^{\cdots} = \log_a \ldots\ldots$

$\log_a \ldots\ldots + \log_a 7 = \log_a (\ldots\ldots \times \ldots\ldots)$

$\qquad\qquad\qquad = \log_a \ldots\ldots$

> Use $\log_a (x^n) = n\log_a x$ to write $3\log_a 2$ in the form $\log_a 2^n$.

> Use $\log_a x + \log_a y = \log_a (xy)$ to combine the two logarithms and simplify.

2.   Find

(a) the value of p such that $\log_4 p = -2$ (2)

....

....

(b) the value of y such that $\log_y 125 = 3$ (2)

....

....

(c) the value of $\log_8 16$ (2)

....

....

....

> You can use the change of base formula to write $\log_8 16$ as a logarithm to base 2, that is, $\log_a x = \dfrac{\log_b x}{\log_b a}$

3.   Express as a single logarithm to base a

(a) $2\log_a 5 + 3\log_a 2$ (2)

....

....

(b) $4\log_a 3 - \log_a 12$ (2)

....

....

> **Guided**   4.   Given that $y = 4x^3$, show that $\log_4 y = 1 + 3\log_4 x$ (3)

$\log_4 y = \log_4 4x^3$

$\log_4 y = \log_4 \ldots\ldots + \log_4 \ldots\ldots$

$\log_4 y = \ldots\ldots + \ldots\ldots \log_4 \ldots\ldots$

> Take logs on both sides, then use $\log_a m + \log_a n = \log_a (mn)$ to write as the sum of two separate log terms.

> Remember that $\log_a a = 1$.

5.   Given that $y^2 = 9x^4$, show that $\log_3 y = 1 + 2\log_3 x$ (3)

....

....

....

Equations with logs

Guided **1.** Find the value of x for which $\log_3(2x-1) - \log_3 x = 1$ **(4)**

$$\log_3\left(\frac{\rule{3cm}{0.4pt}}{\rule{3cm}{0.4pt}}\right) = 1$$

$$\frac{\rule{2cm}{0.4pt}}{\rule{2cm}{0.4pt}} = 3\cdots$$

> Use $\log_a m - \log_a n = \log_a\left(\frac{m}{n}\right)$ to combine the two log expressions on the left-hand side.

> Use $\log_a b = n \leftrightarrow a^n = b$, then rearrange the equation to solve for x.

2. Solve the equation $\log_2(x+2) - \log_2 x = \log_2 5$ **(3)**

Guided **3.** Given that a and b are positive constants, solve the simultaneous equations

$$a = 4b \quad ①$$
$$\log_2 a + \log_2 b = 3 \quad ②$$

Give your answers as exact numbers. **(6)**

> Substitute ① into ②.

$$\log_2\rule{1cm}{0.4pt} + \log_2 b = 3$$

> Combine the log terms and apply $\log_a b = x \leftrightarrow a^x = b$.

> Remember that a and b are **positive** and give **exact** values.

4. (a) Given that $2\log_2(x-2) - \log_2(6-x) = 1$, show that $x^2 - 2x - 8 = 0$ **(5)**

(b) Hence, or otherwise, solve $2\log_2(x-2) - \log_2(6-x) = 1$ **(2)**

> Remember that $\log_a b$ is only defined for $b > 0$.

5. Find the values of x such that $\dfrac{\log_3 81 + \log_3 243}{\log_3 x} = \log_3 x$ **(5)**

Exponential equations

Guided

1. (a) Find, to 3 significant figures, the value of x for which $3^x = 5$ **(2)**

$3^x = 5$

$\log 3^x = \log 5$

$x \log 3 = \log 5$

$x = \dfrac{\cdots\cdots\cdots}{\cdots\cdots} = \cdots\cdots\cdots\cdots$

> Take logs on both sides or make use of the log■☐ key.

> Rearrange the equation to find x. Then use the log key.

(b) Solve the equation $3^{2x} - 8(3^x) + 15 = 0$ **(4)**

Let $Y = 3^x$ so $3^{2x} = (3^x)^2 = Y^{\cdots\cdots}$

$Y^2 - 8Y + 15 = 0$

$(Y\cdots\cdots)(Y\cdots\cdots) = 0$

$Y = \cdots\cdots$ or $Y = \cdots\cdots$ so $3^x = \cdots\cdots$ or $3^x = \cdots\cdots$

$x = \cdots\cdots$ or $x = \cdots\cdots$

> Let $Y = 3^x$ then write as a quadratic in Y and factorise.

> Use $a^x = b \leftrightarrow \log_a b = x$ to find the values of x.

2. (a) Sketch the graph of $y = 5^x$, $x \in \mathbb{R}$, showing the coordinates of any points at which the graph crosses the axes.   **(2)**

> Graphs of $y = a^x$ pass through $(0, 1)$ and have $y = 0$ as an asymptote.

(b) Solve the equation $5^{2x} + 3(5^x) - 10 = 0$, giving your answer to 2 decimal places.   **(6)**

> Remember that $a^x > 0$.

....

....

....

3. Sketch the graph of $y = 0.5^x$, $x \in \mathbb{R}$, showing the coordinates of any points at which the graph crosses the axes.   **(2)**

4. Solve the equation $8^{2x} - 8(8^x) + 7 = 0$ **(6)**

....

....

....

Series and logs

Guided   1.   A geometric series has first term 12 and common ratio 2.5
Find the smallest value of n for which the sum of the
first n terms exceeds 20 000   **(4)**

> Remember that in an inequality, if you multiply or divide by a **negative** number, the **direction** of the inequality changes.

$a = \text{............}$ $r = \text{............}$ $S_n = \dfrac{a(1 - r^n)}{1 - r}$

> Remember to round n up to the nearest whole number.

$$\dfrac{12(1 - \text{............})}{1 - \text{............}} > 20\,000$$

....

....

Guided   2.   A motorcycle was purchased for £25 000 on 1 January.
On 1 January each following year, the value of the motorcycle
is 85% of its value on 1 January in the previous year. The value
of the motorcycle falls below £1500 for the first time m years
after it was purchased. Find the value of m.   **(4)**

> You need to identify the first **term** in the series that is less than £1500.

$a = \text{............}$ $r = \text{............}$ $n\text{th term} = ar^{n-1}$

> Remember that if $0 < a < 1$, then $\log a$ is negative.

$\text{............................} < 1500$

....

....

....

....

3.   A geometric series has first term 12 and common ratio 0.8
Find the smallest value of n for which the sum of the first n terms exceeds 40   **(4)**

....

....

....

....

....

4.   The adult population of a town is 250 000 at the end of Year 1. A model predicts that the adult
population of the town will increase by 4% each year, forming a geometric sequence.
The model predicts that Year N will be the first year in which the adult population of the town
exceeds 500 000

(a)   Show that $(N - 1)\log 1.04 > \log 2$ **(3)**

....

....

....

(b)   Find the value of N.   **(2)**

....

....

Stationary points 1

> **Guided**

1. Find the coordinates of the stationary point on the curve with equation $y = 3x^2 - 18x$ (4)

$$\frac{dy}{dx} = \text{.........} x - 18$$

$$\text{.........} x - 18 = 0$$

$$x = \text{............}   y = \text{........................}$$

Coordinates are (............, ...)

> At a **stationary** point or **turning** point $\frac{dy}{dx} = 0$.

> Solve the equation to find x, then substitute the x-value into the equation for y.

> **Guided**

2. The diagram shows part of the curve with equation $y = x^2 - 32\sqrt{x}$

Use calculus to show that y is decreasing for $0 < x < 4$ (4)

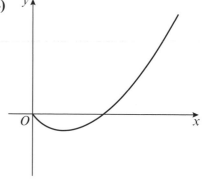

> If y or f(x) is **decreasing**, then $\frac{dy}{dx}$ or f$'(x)$ is negative.

> Solve the inequality to find the condition for x.

$$y = x^2 - 32\sqrt{x} = x^2 - 32x^{\cdots}$$

$$\frac{dy}{dx} = \text{...............................} < 0$$

....

....

3. Find the coordinates of the stationary point on the curve with equation $y = 2x^2 - 8x + 5$ (4)

....

....

....

4. Find the coordinates of the turning points on the curve with equation $y = x^3 - 7x^2 - 5x + 6$ (6)

> There are **two** turning points on this curve. Differentiate first, then solve the quadratic equation by factorising.

....

....

....

....

....

5. The curve C has equation $f(x) = 3x^2 - \frac{2}{x} + 5$

Use calculus to show that f(x) is increasing when $x = 2$ (2)

....

....

....

....

Stationary points 2

1. The curve C has equation $y = 8x^2 - 20x - x^3$

   (a) Use calculus to find the coordinates of the stationary points. **(6)**

   ....

   ....

   ....

   ....

   ....

   (b) Find $\dfrac{d^2y}{dx^2}$ and hence verify the nature of the stationary points. **(3)**

To find $\dfrac{d^2y}{dx^2}$ differentiate twice.

If $\dfrac{d^2y}{dx^2} > 0$, then the turning point is **minimum**.
If $\dfrac{d^2y}{dx^2} < 0$, then the turning point is **maximum**.

   ....

   ....

   ....

> **Guided**

2. The curve C has equation $y = 6\sqrt{x} - 2x^{\frac{3}{2}} + 5, \; x > 0$

   (a) Use calculus to find the coordinates of the turning point on C. **(7)**

   $y = 6x^{\frac{1}{2}} - 2x^{\frac{3}{2}} + 5$ so $\dfrac{dy}{dx} =$ ....

   ....

   ....

   ....

   ....

   (b) Find $\dfrac{d^2y}{dx^2}$ **(2)**

   ....

   ....

   (c) State the nature of the turning point. **(1)**

   ....

   ....

3. The curve C has equation $y = 8 - 2x - \dfrac{6}{x^3}, \; x \neq 0$

   (a) Use calculus to find the exact values of the x-coordinates of the stationary points. **(5)**

   ....

   ....

   ....

   ....

   (b) Find $\dfrac{d^2y}{dx^2}$ and hence verify the nature of the stationary points. **(3)**

   ....

   ....

Max and min problems

> **Guided**

1. The diagram shows an open-topped cardboard box, in the shape of a cuboid. The base of the box is a rectangle x centimetres by $2x$ centimetres. The height of the box is y centimetres. The volume of the box is $8000\,\text{cm}^3$.

(a) Show that the area, $A\,\text{cm}^2$, of the cardboard used to make the box is given by $A = \dfrac{24\,000}{x} + 2x^2$ **(4)**

Volume $= 2x^2y = 8000$

$y = \dfrac{8000}{\ldots\ldots} = \ldots\ldots\ldots$ $A = \ldots\ldots\ldots\ldots\ldots\ldots\ldots\ldots\ldots\ldots\ldots\ldots$

$\ldots\ldots$

> First find an equation connecting x and y using the formula for the volume of the cuboid, then write y in terms of x. Simplify your answer.

> Work out an expression for A in terms of x, remembering the box is open topped.

....

....

(b) Use calculus to find the value of x for which A is stationary, correct to 3 significant figures. **(4)**

> Differentiate the expression for A and put equal to 0, then solve to find the value of x which gives a stationary value.

....

....

....

(c) Prove that this value of x gives a minimum value of A. **(2)**

> Find $\dfrac{\text{d}^2 A}{\text{d}x^2}$ and substitute the value of x. Remember to write a statement to say what your answer shows.

....

....

(d) Calculate the minimum area of cardboard needed to make the box. **(2)**

....

> Substitute the value of x into the equation for A to find the area of cardboard needed.

....

2. A solid right circular cylinder has radius r cm and height h cm as shown in the diagram. The total surface area of the cylinder is $900\,\text{cm}^2$.

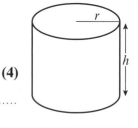

(a) Show that the volume, $V\,\text{cm}^3$, of the cylinder is given by $V = 450r - \pi r^3$ **(4)**

....

....

....

(b) Given that r varies, use calculus to find the maximum value of V, to the nearest cm^3. **(6)**

....

....

....

(c) Justify that the value of V you have found is a maximum. **(2)**

....

....

Definite integration

Guided 1. Use calculus to find $\int_1^2 (x^3 - 3x^2 + 5x - 7)\,dx$ (4)

$$\int_1^2 (x^3 - 3x^2 + 5x - 7)\,dx = \left[\frac{x^{\cdots}}{\cdots} - x^3 + \cdots\cdots\cdots \right]_1^2$$

$$= (\cdots\cdots\cdots\cdots\cdots) - (\cdots\cdots\cdots\cdots\cdots)$$

$$= \cdots\cdots - \cdots\cdots = \cdots\cdots$$

Guided 2. Use calculus to find the exact value of $\int_1^2 \left(2x^2 + 3 - \frac{5}{x^2}\right)dx$ (5)

$$\int_1^2 \left(2x^2 + 3 - \frac{5}{x^2}\right)dx = \int_1^2 (2x^2 + 3 - 5x^{\cdots})\,dx$$

$$= \left[\frac{2x^{\cdots}}{\cdots} + 3\cdots\cdots\cdots\cdots \right]_1^2$$

$$= (\cdots\cdots\cdots\cdots\cdots) - (\cdots\cdots\cdots\cdots\cdots)$$

$$= \cdots\cdots - \cdots\cdots = \cdots\cdots$$

> Write every term in the polynomial in the form ax^n before integrating.

3. Use calculus to find the value of $\int_1^4 (5x - 3\sqrt{x})\,dx$ (5)

> Dividing by $\frac{a}{b}$ is the same as multiplying by $\frac{b}{a}$.

4. Evaluate $\int_2^8 \left(x + \frac{2}{\sqrt{x}}\right)dx$, giving your answer in the form $a + b\sqrt{2}$, where a and b are integers.   (5)

5. Use calculus to find the exact value of $\int_1^2 \left(\frac{3}{x^4} - \frac{2}{x^3} + 5\right)dx$ (5)

Area under a curve

Guided   1.   The diagram shows part of the curve with equation $y = (x + 1)(3 - x)$

Use calculus to find the exact area of the shaded region, R.   **(5)**

> First expand the brackets before integrating.

> The limits for the definite integral are the values of x where the graph crosses the x-axis.

Graph crosses x-axis at $x =$ .... and $x =$ ....

$y = 3 + 2x - x^2$

$\int_{....}^{3} \left(3 + 2x - x^2 \right) dx = \left[............................ \right]_{....}^{3}$

$\qquad = (............................) - (............................)$

$\qquad = ... - .... = ...$

Area = ...

Guided   2.   The diagram shows part of the curve with equation
$y = (x + 2)(x - 4)$

Find the area of the shaded region, R.   **(5)**

> The area is below the x-axis so the definite integral gives a **negative** answer. Remember to write the **positive** value as your answer.

Graph crosses x-axis at $x =$ .... and $x =$ ....

$y = ...$

$\int_{....}^{....} \left(............................ \right) dx = \left[............................ \right]_{....}^{....}$

$\qquad = (............................) - (............................)$

$\qquad = ... = ...$

Area = ...

3.   The diagram shows part of the curve C with equation $y = x(x - 2)(x - 6)$

Use calculus to find the total area of the finite region, shown shaded in the diagram, that is between $x = 0$ and $x = 4$ and is bounded by C, the x-axis and the line $x = 4$ **(9)**

....

....

....

....

....

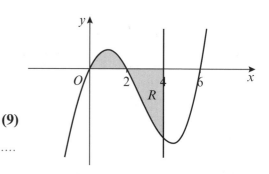

> You need to work out two separate integrals and add the areas together, because an area below the x-axis will produce a **negative** integral.

More areas

1. The diagram shows part of the curve C with equation $y = x^2 - 6x + 8$

The points L and M have coordinates $(2, 0)$ and $(4, 0)$ respectively. The point N lies on the curve and has x-coordinate 6. The shaded region R is bounded by the curve, the x-axis and the line segment LN. Find the exact area of R. **(7)**

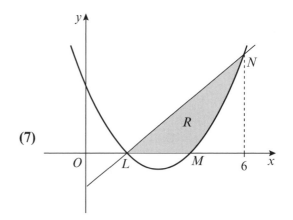

$L\ (2,\ 0);\ M\ (4,\ 0)\quad$ At N: $x = 6$, $y = $ ....

Area of triangle $= \dfrac{1}{2} \times$ base $\times$ height

$\qquad\qquad\qquad = \dfrac{1}{2} \times$ .... $\times$ ....

$\qquad\qquad\qquad = $ ....

$\displaystyle\int_4^6 \left(x^2 - 6x + 8\right) dx = \left[\dfrac{x^3}{3} - \text{.............} + \text{.............}\right]_4^6$

$\qquad\qquad\qquad = \left[\text{.............} - \text{.............}\right]_4^6$

$\qquad\qquad\qquad = \text{.........................} = \text{.........................}$

Area of $R = $ .... $-$ .... $= $ ....

> You need to find the area of the triangle and the area under C between $x = 4$ and $x = 6$.

> Area of $R =$ area of triangle $-$ area under C

2. The line with equation $y = 20 - 3x$ cuts the curve with equation $y = x^2 + 2x + 14$ at the points A and B, as shown in the diagram.

(a) Use algebra to find the coordinates of A and the coordinates of B. **(5)**

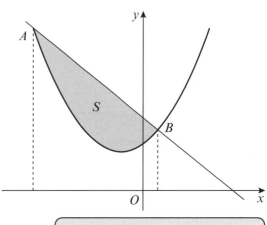

....

....

....

....

....

> Solve the equations simultaneously.

....

....

The shaded region S is bounded by the line and the curve, as shown in the diagram.

(b) Use calculus to find the exact area of S. **(7)**

....

....

> Find the area of the trapezium and the area under the curve between A and B.

....

> Area of $S =$ area of trapezium $-$ area under C

....

....

....

....

The trapezium rule

Guided 1. $y = \sqrt{4^x + x}$

(a) Complete the table below, giving the values of y to 2 decimal places. **(2)**

x	0	0.2	0.4	0.6	0.8	1
y	1	1.23	1.46			2.24

> Make sure you write your answers to the degree of accuracy asked for in the question.

$x = 0.4:\ y = \sqrt{4^{0.4} + 0.4} = 1.463$

(b) Use the trapezium rule, with all the values of y from your table, to find an approximate value for $\int_0^1 \sqrt{4^x + x}\,dx$ **(4)**

> The trapezium rule states that
> $$\int_a^b y\,dx \approx \tfrac{1}{2}h\{(y_0 + y_n) + 2(y_1 + y_2 + \ldots + y^{n-1})\}$$
> where $h = \dfrac{b-a}{n}$

$a = \ldots\ldots\ldots\ldots$ $b = \ldots\ldots\ldots\ldots$

$n = 6 - 1 = 5$

> n represents the number of strips which is **1 less** than the number of values in the table. As a check, h is also the difference between the x-values.

$h = \dfrac{\ldots\ldots\ldots\ldots}{5} = \ldots\ldots\ldots\ldots$

$\int_0^1 \sqrt{4^x + x}\,dx \approx \dfrac{1}{2} \ldots\ldots\ldots\{(1 + 2.24) + 2(1.23 + \ldots\ldots\ldots\ldots + \ldots\ldots\ldots\ldots + \ldots\ldots\ldots\ldots)\}$

$= \ldots\ldots\ldots\ldots\ldots\ldots\ldots\ldots\ldots\ldots\ldots\ldots\ldots\ldots \quad = \ldots\ldots\ldots\ldots\ldots\ldots$

2. $y = \dfrac{4x}{\sqrt{2 + x}}$

(a) Complete the table below, giving the values of y to 2 decimal places. **(2)**

x	1	1.1	1.2	1.3	1.4	1.5
y	2.31		2.68			3.21

(b) Use the trapezium rule, with all the values of y in the completed table, to obtain an approximate value for $\int_1^{1.5} \dfrac{4x}{\sqrt{2+x}}\,dx$, giving your answer to 1 decimal place. **(4)**

....

....

....

....

3. $y = \dfrac{20}{2x^2 - 1}$

(a) Complete the table below, giving the values of y to 3 decimal places. **(2)**

x	2	2.25	2.5	2.75	3
y	2.857		1.739		1.176

(b) Use the trapezium rule, with all the values of y from your table, to find an approximate value for $\int_2^3 \dfrac{20}{2x^2 - 1}\,dx$, giving your answer to 2 decimal places. **(4)**

....

....

....

....

You are the examiner!

Checking through your work is a key skill for AS maths. Have a look at pages 56 and 57 of the *Revision Guide*, then practise with these questions. There are full worked solutions on page 167.

1. The line joining points $(-2, 3)$ and $(4, 7)$ is a diameter of the circle C.

   Find an equation for C. **(6)**

   > You first need to find the coordinates of the **centre** of the circle, which is the midpoint of the line joining the two given points.

   > The right-hand side of the circle equation is r **squared**. Be careful to distinguish between the length of the **diameter** and the length of the **radius**.

2. (a) Find the first 4 terms of the binomial expansion, in ascending powers of x, of
   $$\left(1 + \frac{x}{4}\right)^{10}$$
   giving each term in its simplest form. **(4)**

   > The binomial expansion in the formulae booklet is for $(a + b)^n$. Remember to put the b term in brackets when you substitute.

   (b) Use your expansion to estimate the value of $(1.05)^{10}$, giving your answer to 4 decimal places. **(3)**

   > To work out the value of x to substitute, solve $1 + \frac{x}{4} = 1.05$. Remember to give your answer to the degree of accuracy stated in the question.

You are the examiner!

> Checking through your work is a key skill for AS maths. Have a look at pages 56 and 57 of the *Revision Guide*, then practise with these questions. There are full worked solutions on page 167.

3. Solve, for $0 \leqslant x < 180°$, $\sin(2x + 20°) = -0.3$, giving your answers to 1 decimal place. You should show each step in your working. **(7)**

> Remember to **transform** the range. If $0 \leqslant x < 180°$, then $20° \leqslant 2x + 20° < 380°$.

> Let $Z = 2x + 20°$. Find the first value of Z by using your calculator to work out $\sin^{-1}(-0.3)$, then use a sketch of $y = \sin Z$ to help you find the second value. Finally, rearrange $Z = 2x + 20$ to find the values of x.

....

....

....

....

....

....

....

4. (a) Given that $\log_2(2x + 10) = 2\log_2(x - 1) + 1$, show that $x^2 - 3x - 4 = 0$ **(5)**

....

....

....

....

....

(b) Hence, or otherwise, solve
$$\log_2(2x + 10) = 2\log_2(x - 1) + 1$$ **(2)**

> Remember that $\log_a b$ exists only if $b > 0$.

....

....

....

5. Find the coordinates of the stationary point on the curve with equation $y = 4x^2 - 4x + 5$ **(4)**

> At a **stationary** point or **turning** point $\frac{dy}{dx} = 0$.

> Solve the equation to find x, then substitute the x-value into the equation for y to find **both** coordinates.

....

....

....

....

....

....

....

Constant acceleration 1

Guided > 1. A car moves with constant acceleration along a straight horizontal road. The car passes the point A with speed $5\,\text{m s}^{-1}$ and 4 s later it passes the point B, with a speed of $20\,\text{m s}^{-1}$.

(a) Find the acceleration of the car. **(2)**

$s = ?$ $u = 5$ $v = 20$ $a = ?$ $t = 4$

$v = u + at$

$\text{..........} = \text{..........} + a \times 4$

....

....

> Constant acceleration means using the **suvat** formulae. Write down the five letters and all the values you know.

> Use $v = u + at$ and solve to find a.

(b) Find the distance AB. **(2)**

$s = ?$ $u = 5$ $v = 20$ $a = \text{.........}$ $t = 4$

$s = \frac{1}{2}(\text{.....................})\text{......} = \text{...}\ \text{m}$

> Use $s = \frac{1}{2}(u + v)t$.

> Note you could also use $s = ut + \frac{1}{2}at^2$ or $s = vt - \frac{1}{2}at^2$ using the value of a calculated in part (a). However, it is safer to use **given** values, than to use **calculated** values.

2. A particle P is moving with constant acceleration along a straight horizontal line ABC where $AC = 25\,\text{m}$. Initially P is at A and is moving with speed $6\,\text{m s}^{-1}$ in the direction AB. After 2.5 s, P is at B with speed $10.5\,\text{m s}^{-1}$.

> When the question involves **three points** draw a quick sketch to help you.

(a) Find the acceleration of the particle. **(2)**

....

....

....

(b) Find the distance BC. **(3)**

....

....

....

3. The driver of a train begins the approach to a station by applying the brakes when the speed is $40\,\text{m s}^{-1}$. The train takes 30 s to come to rest at the station.

> When the train comes to rest, $v = 0$.

(a) Find the deceleration of the train. **(2)**

....

....

(b) Find the distance between the train and the station when the driver applied the brakes. **(2)**

....

....

Constant acceleration 2

Guided   **1.** Three posts P, Q and R, are fixed in that order at the side of a straight horizontal road. The distance from P to Q is 45 m and the distance from Q to R is 120 m. A car is moving along the road with constant acceleration a m s^{-2}. The speed of the car, as it passes P, is u m s^{-1}. The car passes Q 2 s after passing P, and the car passes R 4 s after passing Q.

Find the value of u and the value of a.   (7)

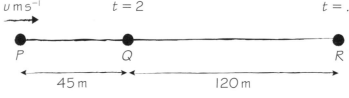

PQ: $s = 45$ $u = u$ $\cancel{v = ?}$ $a = a$ $t = 2$

     $45 = u \times \dots\dots + \frac{1}{2}a \times \dots\dots^2$ ①

PR: $s = \dots\dots$ $u = u$ $\cancel{v = ?}$ $a = a$ $t = \dots\dots$

     $\dots\dots = u \times \dots\dots + \frac{1}{2}a \times \dots\dots^2$ ②

> When the question involves **three points**, draw a quick sketch to help you.

> Use $s = ut + \frac{1}{2}at^2$ for PQ and PR and solve simultaneously.

....

....

....

....

2. Two cars A and B are moving in the same direction along a straight horizontal road. At time $t = 0$, they are side by side, passing a point O on the road. Car A travels at a constant speed of 40 m s^{-1}. Car B passes O with a speed of 25 m s^{-1}, and has constant acceleration of 5 m s^{-2}. Find

(a) the speed of B when it has travelled 80 m from O (2)   > Use $v^2 = u^2 + 2as$ for B.

....

....

(b) the distance from O of A when B is 80 m from O (4)

> Find the time taken for B to travel 80 m from O.

....

> For constant speed, $a = 0$ so you can use $s = vt$.

....

(c) the time when B overtakes A.   (5)

> Find the time when the cars are the same distance from O.

....

....

....

....

Motion under gravity

Guided 1. A ball is projected vertically upwards with speed 21 m s⁻¹ from a point A, which is 1.5 m above the ground. After projection, the ball moves freely under gravity until it reaches the ground. Modelling the ball as a particle, find

(a) the greatest height above A reached by the ball **(3)**

$s = ?$ $u = $ .... $v = 0$ $a = -9.8$ ~~$t = ?$~~

$v^2 = u^2 + 2as$ so $0^2 = $ ....$^2 - 2 \times 9.8 \times h$

$h = $ ....

> Remember that at the greatest height, $v = 0$. When travelling upwards, acceleration is negative and due to gravity, so use $a = -9.8$ m s⁻².

(b) the speed of the ball as it reaches the ground **(3)**

$s = $ .... $+ 1.5$ $u = 0$ $v = ?$ $a = 9.8$ ~~$t = ?$~~

$v^2 = u^2 + 2as$ so $v^2 = 0^2 + 2 \times 9.8 \times$ ....

$v = $ ....

> When travelling downwards, acceleration is positive and due to gravity, so use $a = 9.8$ m s⁻².

> Remember that the ball started 1.5 m above the ground.

(c) the time between the instant when the ball is projected from A and the instant when the ball reaches the ground. **(4)**

~~$s = ?$~~ $u = 21$ $v = $ .... $a = -9.8$ $t = ?$

$v = u + at$

> Considering upwards motion, velocity when the ball lands will be **negative**.

....

....

Guided 2. A firework rocket starts from rest at ground level and moves vertically. In the first 4 s of its motion, the rocket rises 50 m. The rocket is modelled as a particle moving with constant acceleration a m s⁻². Find

(a) the value of a **(2)**

$s = $ .... $u = 0$ ~~$v = ?$~~ $a = ?$ $t = $ ....

> Use $s = ut + \frac{1}{2}at^2$.

....

....

(b) the speed of the rocket 4 s after it has left the ground. **(2)**

> Use $v = u + at$.

....

....

After 4 s, the rocket burns out. The motion of the rocket is now modelled as that of a particle moving freely under gravity.

(c) Find the height of the rocket above the ground 7 s after it has left the ground. **(4)**

> Consider motion from $t = 4$ to $t = 7$; use $s = ut + \frac{1}{2}at^2$.

....

....

....

....

Speed–time graphs

Guided 1. A car is moving along a straight horizontal road. The speed of the car as it passes the point A is $30\,\text{m s}^{-1}$ and the car maintains this speed for $40\,\text{s}$. The car then decelerates uniformly to a speed of $20\,\text{m s}^{-1}$. The speed of $20\,\text{m s}^{-1}$ is then maintained until the car passes the point B. The time taken to travel from A to B is $100\,\text{s}$ and $AB = 2500\,\text{m}$.

   (a) Sketch a speed–time graph to show the motion of the car from A to B. (2)

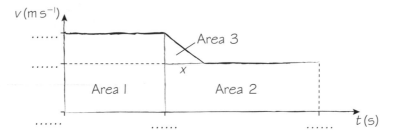

> Divide the area under the graph into separate sections to calculate the total area.

   (b) Calculate the deceleration of the car as it decelerates from $30\,\text{m s}^{-1}$ to $20\,\text{m s}^{-1}$. (7)

   Area = Area 1 + Area 2 + Area 3

   Area = $(30 \times 40) + (20 \times \text{........}) + (\frac{1}{2} \times \text{........} \times x) = 2500$

   $x = \text{........................}$

   Deceleration = $\dfrac{\text{........}}{\text{........}} = \text{........}\,\text{m s}^{-2}$

> Distance travelled = area under graph

> Find the gradient of the graph to work out the deceleration.

2. A train is travelling at $12\,\text{m s}^{-1}$ on a straight horizontal track. The driver sees a red signal $150\,\text{m}$ ahead and immediately applies the brakes. The train immediately decelerates with constant deceleration for $10\,\text{s}$, reducing its speed to $4\,\text{m s}^{-1}$. The driver then releases the brakes and allows the train to travel at a constant speed of $4\,\text{m s}^{-1}$ for a further $10\,\text{s}$. He then applies the brakes again and the train slows down with constant deceleration, coming to rest as it reaches the signal.

   (a) Sketch a speed–time graph to show the motion of the train. (3)

   (b) Find the distance travelled by the train from the moment when the brakes are first applied to the moment when its speed first reaches $4\,\text{m s}^{-1}$. (2)

   ....

   ....

   ....

   (c) Find the total time from the moment when the brakes are first applied to the moment when the train comes to rest. (5)

   ....

   ....

   ....

   ....

Other motion graphs

> **Guided**

1. The diagram shows a speed–time graph for the motion of a car.

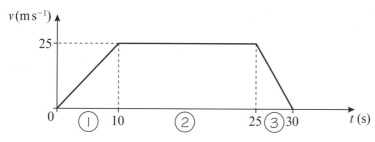

Sketch an acceleration–time graph for the motion of the car. **(5)**

①: $a = \dfrac{\text{.........}}{\text{.........}}$ ②: $a = \text{.........}$ ③: $a = -\dfrac{\text{.........}}{\text{.........}}$

> Work out the gradient for each section of the speed–time graph to find the acceleration or deceleration.

> Use dotted vertical lines to show a change in acceleration.

2. A man travels in a lift to the top of a tall office block. The lift starts from rest on the ground floor and moves vertically. It comes to rest again at the top floor, having moved a vertical distance of 110 m. The lift initially accelerates with a constant acceleration of $4\,\mathrm{m\,s^{-2}}$ until it reaches a speed of $10\,\mathrm{m\,s^{-1}}$. It then moves with a constant speed of $10\,\mathrm{m\,s^{-1}}$ for T seconds. Finally it decelerates with a constant deceleration for 2 s before coming to rest at the top floor.

   (a) Sketch a speed–time graph for the motion of the lift. **(2)**

   (b) Hence, or otherwise, find the value of T. **(3)**

   ....

   ....

   ....

   ....

   (c) Sketch an acceleration–time graph for the motion of the lift. **(3)**

Forces

> **Guided**

1. A breakdown van of mass 2500 kg is towing a car of mass 1500 kg along a straight horizontal road. The two vehicles are joined by a tow-bar which remains parallel to the road. The van and the car experience constant resistances to motion of magnitudes 900 N and 250 N respectively. There is a constant driving force acting on the van of 2750 N. Find

> Draw a clear diagram to help you see what is going on. Consider the **resultant** force in the direction of motion.

(a) the magnitude of the acceleration of the van and the car **(3)**

> Consider the breakdown van and the car as a single system and apply $F = ma$.

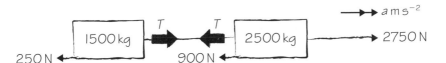

Van and car: 2750 − .... − .... = (2500 + 1500)a

....

....

> The two components of tension in the tow-bar are **equal and opposite** and so cancel out.

(b) the tension in the tow-bar. **(4)**

Car: T − .... = 1500a

....

....

....

> Consider the forces acting **either** on the breakdown van **or** on the car and apply $F = ma$.

> The value of a is the same for the breakdown van and the car.

2. A man of mass 85 kg travels in a lift of mass 900 kg to the top of a tall building. The lift starts from rest on the ground floor and moves vertically upwards with an acceleration of $3 \, \text{m s}^{-2}$. It then moves with constant speed and finally decelerates with a constant deceleration of $2 \, \text{m s}^{-2}$ before coming to rest at the top floor. The lift is pulled up by means of a vertical cable attached to the top of the lift. By modelling the cable as light and inextensible, find

> The force due to gravity on a mass m kg is mg N. Take $g = 9.8 \, \text{m s}^{-2}$.

(a) the tension in the cable when the lift is accelerating **(3)**

....

....

....

(b) the magnitude of the force exerted by the lift on the man when the lift is decelerating. **(3)**

....

....

....

Resolving forces

Guided **1.** A truck of mass 1750 kg is towing a car of mass 750 kg along a straight horizontal road. The two vehicles are joined by a light tow-bar which is inclined at an angle θ to the road, as shown in the diagram. The vehicles are travelling at 20 m s^{-1} as they enter a zone where the speed limit is 14 m s^{-1}. The truck's brakes are applied to give a constant braking force on the truck. The distance travelled between the instant when the brakes are applied and the instant when the speed of each vehicle is 14 m s^{-1} is 100 m.

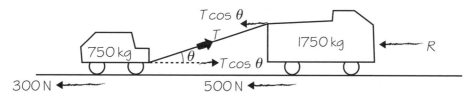

(a) Find the deceleration of the truck and the car. **(3)**

$v^2 = u^2 + 2as$: $14^2 =$ ....

Deceleration = ...

The constant braking force on the truck has magnitude R newtons. The truck and the car also experience constant resistances to motion of 500 N and 300 N respectively.

Given that $\cos\theta = 0.9$, find

(b) the force in the tow-bar **(4)**

$T\cos\theta - 300 =$ ....

....

....

> Consider the forces acting on the car and apply $F = ma$ horizontally.

> The component of T in a horizontal direction is $T\cos\theta$.

(c) the value of R. **(4)**

$-T\cos\theta - 500 - R =$ ....

$R =$ .... N

> Consider the forces acting on the truck and apply $F = ma$ horizontally.

2. A body of mass 5 kg is sliding down a smooth plane inclined at 30° to the horizontal. Find

(a) the acceleration of the mass **(3)**

....

....

....

> Consider the forces acting parallel to the plane and apply $F = ma$.

(b) the normal reaction exerted by the plane on the mass. **(2)**

....

....

....

....

....

> Consider the forces acting perpendicular to the plane. As there is no motion in this direction, the resultant force is 0.

Friction

> **Guided**

1. A sledge is pulled in a straight line with constant speed along horizontal ground by means of a rope. The rope makes an angle of 20° with the horizontal, as shown in the diagram.

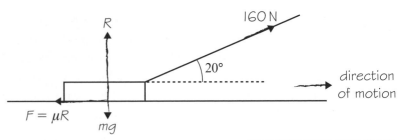

The coefficient of friction between the sledge and the ground is 0.3. The sledge is modelled as a particle and the rope as a light inextensible string.
The tension in the rope is 160 N. Find, to 3 significant figures

(a) the normal reaction of the ground on the sledge **(3)**

$R(\rightarrow)$: $160 \cos 20° - F = 0$

$F = $ ....

but $F = \mu R = 0.3R$, so $R = $ .... N

(b) the mass of the sledge. **(3)**

$R(\uparrow)$: $R + $ .... $- mg = 0$

....

....

> *The sledge moves with constant speed, so the resultant force is 0.*

> *Friction (F) opposes motion. The sledge is moving so $F = \mu R$.*

> *First resolve forces horizontally.*

> *Resolve forces vertically.*

2. A heavy suitcase S of mass 45 kg is moving along a horizontal floor under the action of a force of magnitude P newtons. The force acts at 40° to the floor, as shown in the diagram, and S moves in a straight line at constant speed. The suitcase is modelled as a particle and the floor as a rough horizontal plane. The coefficient of friction between S and the floor is $\frac{2}{3}$.
Calculate the value of P. **(9)**

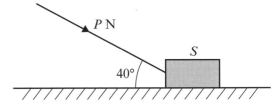

....

....

....

....

....

....

....

....

Sloping planes

> **Guided**

1. A box of mass 4 kg is pulled up a rough plane by means of a light rope. The plane is inclined at an angle of 30° to the horizontal, as shown in the diagram. The rope is parallel to a line of greatest slope of the plane. The tension in the rope is 40 N. The coefficient of friction between the box and the plane is 0.5. By modelling the box as a particle, find

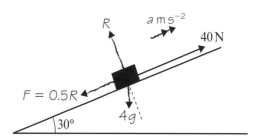

(a) the normal reaction of the plane on the box   **(3)**

$R(\nwarrow): \quad R - 4g\cos 30° = 0$

$R = $ ....

> Resolve the forces perpendicular to the plane. As there is no motion in this direction, the resultant force is 0.

(b) the acceleration of the box.   **(5)**

> Resolve the forces along the plane and apply $F = ma$.

$R(\nearrow): \quad 40 - $ .... $- F = 4a$

$F = \mu R = 0.5 \times $ .... $= $ ....

> Friction (F) opposes motion. The box is moving so $F = \mu R$. Make sure you don't confuse friction with force due to gravity.

....

....

2. A particle of mass 1 kg is held at rest on a rough plane. The plane is inclined at an angle α to the horizontal, where $\tan \alpha = \frac{5}{12}$. The particle is released from rest and slides down a line of greatest slope of the plane. The particle moves 2.5 m during the first 2 seconds of its motion. Find

(a) the acceleration of the particle   **(3)**

....

....

(b) the coefficient of friction between the particle and the plane.   **(5)**

....

> 5-12-13 is a right-angled triangle.

....

....

3. A particle P of mass 5 kg is moving up a fixed rough plane at constant speed under the action of a force of magnitude 40 N. The plane is inclined at 20° to the horizontal. The force acts in the vertical plane containing the line of greatest slope of the plane through P, and acts at 20° to the inclined plane, as shown in the diagram. The coefficient of friction between P and the plane is μ. Find

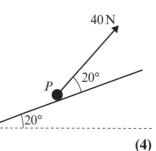

(a) the magnitude of the normal reaction between P and the plane   **(4)**

....

....

(b) the value of μ.   **(5)**

....

....

Pulleys

> **Guided**

1. The particles A and B have masses 4 kg and m kg respectively, where $m < 4$. They are attached to the ends of a light inextensible string. The string passes over a smooth pulley which is fixed. The particles are held in position with the string taut and the hanging parts of the string vertical, at a height of 3 m above the floor, as shown in the diagram. The particles are then released from rest and in the subsequent motion B does reach the pulley. The initial acceleration of each particle has magnitude $\frac{4}{7}g$. Find

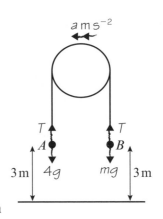

As $m < 4$, A will move down and B will move up. Apply $F = ma$ for each particle.

As the pulley is smooth, the tension in the string is the same for both particles.

(a) the tension in the string immediately after the particles are released **(3)**

A: $4g - T = 4a$

Apply $F = ma$ on A.

....

(b) the value of m. **(4)**

B: $T - mg = ma$

Apply $F = ma$ on B.

....

....

When the particles have been moving for 0.5 s, the string breaks.

(c) Find the further time that elapses until B hits the floor. **(9)**

First find the velocity of B after 0.5 s, then find the distance travelled upwards in this time.

($\uparrow$): $v = u + at =$ .... = ...

($\uparrow$): $s = ut + \frac{1}{2}at^2 =$ .... = ...

($\downarrow$): $s = ut + \frac{1}{2}at^2$

Finally, find the time taken for B to fall from the height where the string broke to the floor.

....

....

....

....

2. Two particles A and B have masses $4m$ and km respectively, where $k > 4$. They are connected by a light inextensible string which passes over a smooth fixed pulley. The system is released from rest with the string taut and the hanging parts of the string vertical, as shown in the diagram. While the particles are moving freely, A has an acceleration of magnitude $\frac{3}{5}g$.

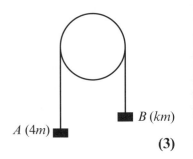

(a) Find, in terms of m and g, the tension in the string. **(3)**

....

....

(b) Find the value of k. **(4)**

....

....

Connected particles 1

> **Guided**

1. The diagram shows two particles P and Q, of masses 4 kg and
5 kg respectively, connected by a light inextensible string.
Initially P is held at rest on a rough fixed plane inclined
at 40° to the horizontal. The coefficient of friction
between P and the plane is 0.4. The string passes
over a small smooth light pulley A fixed at the top
of the plane. The part of the string from P to A is
parallel to a line of greatest slope of the plane.
The particle Q hangs freely below A. The system is released from rest with the string taut. Find

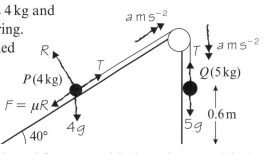

   (a) the acceleration of the system   (8)

   Q: $5g - T = 5a$ ①

   P: $R = 4g \cos 40° = \ \ldots\ldots\ N$

    $T - F - 4g \sin 40° = 4a$ ②

   > Write down the equations of
   > motion for P and Q and solve
   > the equations simultaneously.

   ....

   ....

   ....

   (b) the tension in the string.   (2)

   ....

   ....

   On release, Q is at a height of 0.6 m above the ground.

   (c) Find the speed of Q as it reaches the ground.   (2)   > Use the **suvat** formulae.

   ....

   ....

2. Two particles P and Q have masses $4m$ and $6m$ respectively.
They are connected by a light inextensible string which
passes over a small smooth light pulley fixed at the edge of
a rough horizontal table. Particle P lies on the table and
particle Q hangs freely below the pulley, as shown in the
diagram. The coefficient of friction between P and the table
is 0.5. The system is released from rest with the string taut.
For the period before Q hits the floor or P reaches the pulley

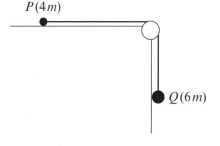

   (a) find, in terms of g, the acceleration of Q (4)

   ....

   ....

   ....

   (b) find, in terms of m and g, the tension in the string.   (2)

   ....

   ....

Connected particles 2

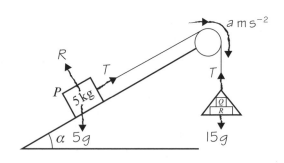

Guided

1. One end of a light inextensible string is attached to a block P of mass 5 kg. The block P is held at rest on a smooth fixed plane which is inclined to the horizontal at an angle α, where $\sin \alpha = \frac{3}{5}$. The string lies along a line of greatest slope of the plane and passes over a smooth light pulley which is fixed at the top of the plane. The other end of the string is attached to a light scale pan which carries two blocks Q and R, with block Q on top of block R, as shown in the diagram. The mass of block Q is 5 kg and the mass of block R is 10 kg. The scale pan hangs at rest and the system is released from rest. By modelling the blocks as particles, ignoring air resistance and assuming the motion is uninterrupted, find

(a) (i) the acceleration of the scale pan

> Write down the equations of motion for P and for the scale pan as a whole, then solve simultaneously.

P: $T - \dots\dots\dots = 5a$ ①

Scale pan: $15g - T = 15a$ ②

① + ②: $15g - \dots\dots\dots = \dots\dots$ $a = \dots\dots$

(ii) the tension in the string   **(8)**

....

....

(b) the magnitude of the force exerted on block Q by block R **(3)**

> Write down the equation of motion for Q.

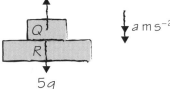

Q: $5g - N = 5 \times \dots\dots$

....

....

(c) the magnitude of the force exerted on the pulley by the string.   **(5)**

> F is equal to the sum of the resolved components of T.

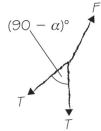

$F = T\cos\left(\dfrac{90 - \alpha}{2}\right)^{\circ} + T\cos\left(\dfrac{90 - \alpha}{2}\right)^{\circ}$

....

....

2. A block P of mass 2 kg is connected by means of a light inextensible string to a light scale pan which carries two blocks Q and R. Q and R have masses m kg and 0.4 kg respectively. The system is released from rest and P accelerates upwards at a rate of 0.98 m s^{-2}. Find

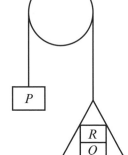

(a) the value of m **(6)**

....

....

....

(b) the magnitude of the force exerted on block R by block Q.   **(3)**

....

Collisions and momentum

> **Guided**

1. A particle P of mass 3 kg is moving along a straight horizontal line with speed $4\,\text{m s}^{-1}$. Another particle Q of mass 3.5 kg is moving, in the opposite direction, along the same straight line with speed $5\,\text{m s}^{-1}$. The particles collide. Immediately after the collision the direction of motion of P is reversed and its speed is $1.5\,\text{m s}^{-1}$.

> Use conservation of momentum: total momentum before = total momentum after, i.e. $m_1u_1 + m_2u_2 = m_1v_1 + m_2v_2$.

(a) Calculate the speed of Q immediately after the impact. **(3)**

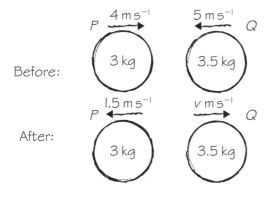

Before:

After:

> Be careful with the **direction** of particles. In this example, label the diagram with **right** as the **positive** direction.

$3 \times 4 + 3.5 \times (-5) = 3 \times (-1.5) + 3.5 \times v$

....

$v = \ldots\ldots\ldots\ldots \text{m s}^{-1}$

so speed $= \ldots\ldots\ldots\ldots \text{m s}^{-1}$

(b) State whether or not the direction of motion of Q is changed by the collision. **(1)**

Direction of Q is ....

> The **sign** of the answer for v will tell you which direction Q is travelling in.

2. Two particles P and Q have masses 3 kg and m kg respectively. They are moving towards each other in opposite directions on a smooth horizontal table. Each particle has speed $6\,\text{m s}^{-1}$ when they collide directly. In this collision, the direction of motion of each particle is reversed. The speed of P immediately after the collision is $3\,\text{m s}^{-1}$ and the speed of Q is $2\,\text{m s}^{-1}$. Find the value of m. **(3)**

....

....

....

....

....

3. Two trucks A and B, moving in opposite directions on the same horizontal railway track, collide. The mass of A is 5000 kg. The mass of B is m kg. Immediately before the collision, the speed of A is $5\,\text{m s}^{-1}$ and the speed of B is $3\,\text{m s}^{-1}$. Immediately after the collision, the trucks are joined together and move with the same speed $2\,\text{m s}^{-1}$. The direction of motion of A is unchanged by the collision. Find the value of m. **(4)**

....

....

....

....

....

Impulse

Guided 1. Two small steel balls A and B have masses 0.8 kg and 0.4 kg respectively. They are moving towards each other in opposite directions on a smooth horizontal table when they collide directly. Immediately before the collision, the speed of A is $9\,\text{m s}^{-1}$ and the speed of B is $3\,\text{m s}^{-1}$. Immediately after the collision, the direction of motion of A is unchanged and the speed of B is 3 times the speed of A. Find

(a) the speed of A immediately after the collision **(5)**

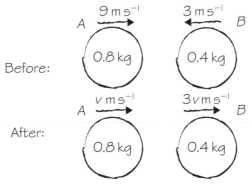

Before:

After:

$0.8 \times 9 + \dots\dots\dots\dots\dots\dots = 0.8 \times v + \dots\dots\dots\dots\dots\dots$

....

....

(b) the magnitude of the impulse exerted on B in the collision. **(3)**

> The impulse on B is the change in momentum, so use $I = mv - mu$.

$I = mv - mu = 0.4 \times \dots\dots\dots\dots\dots\dots = \dots\dots\dots\dots\dots\dots$

....

....

> Remember to consider direction when substituting values of v and u.

2. Two particles P and Q have masses 0.5 kg and 0.4 kg respectively. The particles are initially at rest on a smooth horizontal table. Particle P is given an impulse of magnitude $4\,\text{N s}$ in the direction PQ.

(a) Find the speed of P immediately before it collides with Q. **(3)**

....

....

> The impulse on P is equal to the change in momentum.

....

....

Immediately after the collision between P and Q, the speed of Q is $5\,\text{m s}^{-1}$.

(b) Find the speed of P immediately after the collision. **(3)**

....

....

....

Static particles

Guided 1.

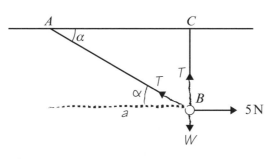

> The bead is in equilibrium, so the **resultant force** in any direction will be **zero**.

> The bead is threaded on a **light inextensible string**, so tension is the **same** throughout the string.

A smooth bead B is threaded on a light inextensible string. The ends of the string are attached to two fixed points A and C on the same horizontal level. The bead is held in equilibrium by a horizontal force of magnitude 5 N acting parallel to AC. The bead B is vertically below C and $\angle BAC = \alpha$, as shown in the diagram. Given that $\tan \alpha = \frac{3}{4}$, find

(a) the tension in the string **(3)**

> To find T resolve forces horizontally.

$R(\rightarrow)$: T...................... $= 5$

$T =$ ....

(b) the weight of the bead. **(4)**

> To find W resolve forces vertically.

$R(\uparrow)$: $T + T$...................... $= W$

2. A particle of mass m kg is attached at C to two light inextensible strings AC and BC. The other ends of the strings are attached to fixed points A and B on a horizontal ceiling. The particle hangs in equilibrium with AC and BC inclined to the horizontal at 20° and 70° respectively, as shown in the diagram. Given that the tension in AC is 15 N, find

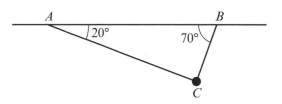

(a) the tension in BC **(4)**

(b) the value of m. **(4)**

3. A particle P of mass 3 kg is held in equilibrium under gravity by two light inextensible strings. One string is horizontal and the other is inclined at an angle α to the horizontal, as shown in the diagram. The tension in the horizontal string is 20 N. The tension in the other string is T newtons.

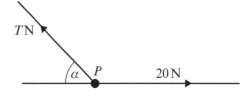

Find the size of the angle α and the value of T. **(8)**

> Resolve horizontally and vertically to find two equations to solve simultaneously.
> Remember that $\frac{\sin \alpha}{\cos \alpha} = \tan \alpha$.

Limiting equilibrium

> **Guided** 1.

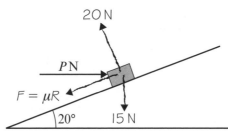

> The parcel is on the point of slipping **up** the plane so $F = \mu R$ and acts down the plane.

A parcel of weight 15 N lies on a rough plane inclined at an angle of 40° to the horizontal. A horizontal force of magnitude P newtons acts on the parcel, as shown in the diagram. The parcel is in equilibrium and on the point of slipping up the plane. The normal reaction of the plane on the parcel is 20 N. The coefficient of friction between the parcel and the plane is μ. Find

(a) the value of P (4)

$R(\nwarrow)$: $P\sin 20° + 15$ .... $= 20$

> Resolve the forces **perpendicular** to the plane.

....

....

(b) the value of μ.   (5)

$R(\nearrow)$: $P\cos 20° = 15$ .... $+ F$

> Resolve the forces **parallel** to the plane and substitute $F = \mu R$.

....

....

The horizontal force is removed.

(c) Determine whether or not the parcel moves.   (5)

$R =$ .... $=$ ....

$F_{max} =$ ....

Component of weight down plane = ...

> First find the **new value** of the **normal reaction** of the plane on the parcel.

....

....

> Compare the component of weight down the plane with the new F_{max} to determine whether or not the parcel will move.

2. A sledge is held in equilibrium on a slope by a rope. The sledge is attached to one end of the rope, the other end being held by a man standing at the top of the slope. The sledge is modelled as a particle of mass 30 kg. The slope is modelled as a rough plane inclined at 50° to the horizontal and the rope as a light inextensible string. The string is assumed to be parallel to a line of greatest slope of the plane, as shown in the diagram. At the contact between the sledge and the slope, the coefficient of friction is 0.25. Find the minimum tension in the rope for the sledge to stay in equilibrium on the slope.   (8)

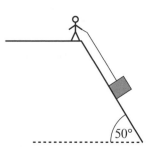

....

....

....

....

Moments 1

Guided 1.

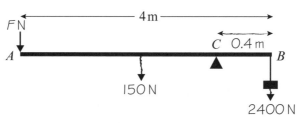

A lever consists of a uniform steel rod AB, of weight 150 N and length 4 m, which rests on a small smooth pivot at a point C of the rod. A load of weight 2400 N is suspended from the end B of the rod by a rope. The lever is held in equilibrium in a horizontal position by a vertical force applied at the end A, as shown in the diagram. The rope is modelled as a light string. Given that $BC = 0.4$ m

(a) find the magnitude of the force applied at A. **(4)**

$\circlearrowleft$ moment about C = 2400 × 0.4

$\circlearrowright$ moment about C = 150 × .... + F × ....

....

....

> The lever is in equilibrium so $\Sigma\circlearrowleft$ moments = $\Sigma\circlearrowright$ moments.
> Remember,
> moment = force × distance.

> Take moments about C so you can ignore the normal reaction.

The position of the pivot is changed so that the rod remains in equilibrium when the force at A has magnitude 150 N.

(b) Find, to the nearest cm, the new distance of the pivot from B. **(5)**

> Let distance $BC = d$ and take moments about C.

$\circlearrowleft$ moment about C = 2400 × d

$\circlearrowright$ moment about C = 150 × .... + 150 × ....

....

....

2. A uniform plank AB has mass 50 kg and length 5 m. It is supported in a horizontal position by two smooth pivots, one at the end A, the other at the point C of the plank where $AC = 3.5$ m, as shown in the diagram. A man of mass 80 kg stands on the plank which remains in equilibrium. The magnitudes of the reactions at the two pivots are each equal to R newtons. By modelling the plank as a rod and the man as a particle, find

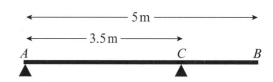

(a) the value of R **(2)**

> The lever is in equilibrium so the resultant of the forces acting in a vertical direction must be zero.

....

....

(b) the distance of the man from A. **(4)**

....

....

....

Moments 2

Guided 1.

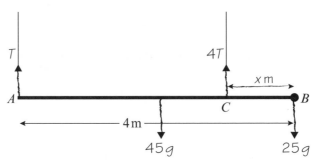

Start by labelling the diagram. Label the tensions T and $4T$ and resolve vertically for the whole system to find T.

A plank AB has mass 45 kg and length 4 m. A load of mass 25 kg is attached to the plank at B. The loaded plank is held in equilibrium, with AB horizontal, by two vertical ropes attached at A and C, as shown in the diagram. The plank is modelled as a uniform rod and the load as a particle. Given that the tension in the rope at C is 4 times the tension in the rope at A, calculate

(a) the tension in the rope at C **(2)**

$R(\uparrow)$: $T + 4T =$ ....

$T =$ .... so $4T =$ ....

(b) the distance CB to the nearest cm. **(5)**

Let $BC = x$, then take moments about C, so you can ignore the component of the tension acting through C.

$\circlearrowleft$ moment about $C =$ ....

$=$ ....

$\circlearrowright$ moment about $C =$ ....

$=$ ....

....

....

2. A heavy uniform steel girder AB has length 12 m. A load of weight 200 N is attached to the girder at A and a load of weight 300 N is attached to the girder at B. The loaded girder hangs in equilibrium in a horizontal position, held by two vertical steel cables attached to the girder at the points C and D, where $AC = 2$ m and $DB = 4$ m, as shown in the diagram.

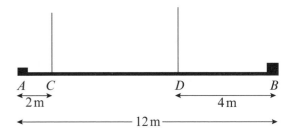

The girder is modelled as a uniform rod, the loads as particles and the cables as light inextensible strings. The tension in the cable at D is three times the tension in the cable at C. Find the tension in the cable at C and the weight of the girder. **(7)**

....

....

....

....

....

....

....

Centres of mass

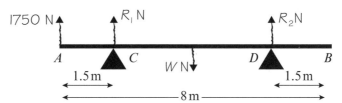

Guided   1. A large log AB is 8 m long. It rests in a horizontal position on two smooth supports C and D, where $AC = 1.5$ m and $BD = 1.5$ m, as shown in the diagram. When a force of magnitude 1750 N is applied vertically upwards to the log at A, the log is about to tilt about D.

(a) Modelling the log as a uniform rod estimate the weight of the log. **(3)**

> If the log is **uniform** the weight will act at the **midpoint**.

↻ moment about $D = 1750 \times$ ....

> Take moments about D so you can ignore the reaction at D.

↺ moment about $D = W \times$ ....

....

....

The log is now modelled as a non-uniform rod.
The force at A is removed and a new force of magnitude 1500 N is applied vertically upwards at B.
The log is now about to tilt about C.

> Taking the distance of the centre of mass as x from C, take moments about D with the 1750 N force at A, then moments about C with the 1500 N force at B. Solve the equations simultaneously.

(b) Find a new estimate for the weight of the log. **(6)**

↻ moment about $D = 1750 \times$ ....   ↻ moment about $C = W \times$ ....

↺ moment about $D = W \times$ ....   ↺ moment about $C = 1500 \times$ ....

....

....

2. A non-uniform rod AB has length 8 m and weight 240 N. The rod rests horizontally in equilibrium on two smooth supports C and D, where

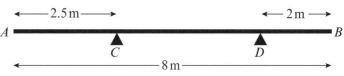

$AC = 2.5$ m and $DB = 2$ m, as shown in the diagram. The centre of mass of AB is x metres from A. A particle of weight W newtons is placed on the rod at A. The rod remains in equilibrium and the magnitude of the reaction of C on the rod is 180 N.

(a) Show that $40x - W = 135$ **(5)**

....

....

The particle is now removed from A and placed on the rod at B. The rod remains in equilibrium and the reaction of C on the rod now has magnitude 60 N.

(b) Calculate the value of x and the value of W. **(6)**

....

....

....

Vectors

Guided 1. A boat B is moving with constant velocity. At noon, B is at the point with position vector $(2\mathbf{i} - 5\mathbf{j})$ km with respect to a fixed origin O. At 1430 on the same day, B is at the point with position vector $(7\mathbf{i} + 10\mathbf{j})$ km.

(a) Find the speed of the boat.   **(4)**

$\underset{\sim}{r} = \underset{\sim}{r_0} + \underset{\sim}{v}t$

$7\underset{\sim}{i} + 10\underset{\sim}{j} = (2\underset{\sim}{i} - 5\underset{\sim}{j}) + \underset{\sim}{v} \times \text{........}$

....

....

....

> Use $\mathbf{r} = \mathbf{r_0} + \mathbf{v}t$ and rearrange for $\mathbf{v}$. If the velocity $\mathbf{v} = (p\mathbf{i} + q\mathbf{j})\,\text{m s}^{-1}$, then speed is $|\mathbf{v}| = \sqrt{p^2 + q^2}$. Alternatively, use the position vectors to calculate the change in displacement.

At time t hours after noon, the position vector of B is $\mathbf{b}$ km.

(b) Find, in terms of t, an expression for $\mathbf{b}$.   **(3)**   > Use $\mathbf{r} = \mathbf{r_0} + \mathbf{v}t$.

....

....

2. A particle P is moving with constant velocity $(-4\mathbf{i} + 3\mathbf{j})\,\text{m s}^{-1}$. At time $t = 5\,\text{s}$, P is at the point with position vector $(-3\mathbf{i} - 6\mathbf{j})\,\text{m}$. Find the distance of P from the origin at time $t = 3\,\text{s}$.   **(5)**

....

....

....

....

> Use $\mathbf{r} = \mathbf{r_0} + \mathbf{v}t$ and rearrange to find the starting point, $\mathbf{r_0}$. If the position vector $\mathbf{r} = (a\mathbf{i} + b\mathbf{j})\,\text{m s}^{-1}$, then distance from origin is $|\mathbf{r}| = \sqrt{a^2 + b^2}$.

3. Two ships P and Q are travelling at night with constant velocities. At midnight, P is at the point with position vector $(12\mathbf{i} + 14\mathbf{j})$ km relative to a fixed origin O. At the same time, Q is at the point with position vector $(8\mathbf{i} - 4\mathbf{j})$ km. Three hours later, P is at the point with position vector $(24\mathbf{i} + 32\mathbf{j})$ km. The ship Q travels with velocity $10\mathbf{j}\,\text{km h}^{-1}$. At time t hours after midnight, the position vectors of P and Q are $\mathbf{p}$ km and $\mathbf{q}$ km respectively. Find

(a) the velocity of P, in terms of $\mathbf{i}$ and $\mathbf{j}$ **(2)**

....

....

(b) expressions for $\mathbf{p}$ and $\mathbf{q}$, in terms of t, $\mathbf{i}$ and $\mathbf{j}$.   **(4)**

....

....

At time t hours after midnight, the distance between P and Q is d km.

(c) By finding an expression for $\overrightarrow{PQ}$ show that $d^2 = 32t^2 - 112t + 340$ **(5)**   > Use $\overrightarrow{PQ} = \mathbf{q} - \mathbf{p}$.

....

....

....

....

....

....

Vectors and bearings

Guided

1. A model boat A moves on a lake with constant velocity $(-2\mathbf{i} + 5\mathbf{j})\,\text{m s}^{-1}$. At time $t = 0$, A is at the point with position vector $(4\mathbf{i} - 7\mathbf{j})\,\text{m}$. Find

   (a) the direction in which A is moving, giving your answer as a bearing. **(3)**

   $\tan\theta = \dfrac{\text{.........}}{\text{.........}} = \text{.........}$ $\theta = \text{.........} \approx \text{.........}°$

   Bearing = ...°

   > Draw a sketch to check which quadrant the boat is moving in.

   At time $t = 0$, a second boat B is at the point with position vector $(-20\mathbf{i} + 5\mathbf{j})\,\text{m}$. Given that the velocity of B is $(2\mathbf{i} + 3\mathbf{j})\,\text{m s}^{-1}$

   (b) show that A and B will collide at a point P and find the position vector of P. **(5)**

   ....

   ....

   ....

   ....

   ....

   > When the boats collide, their position vectors will have the same $\mathbf{i}$ and $\mathbf{j}$ components.

2. A ship S is moving with constant velocity $(2\mathbf{i} - 6\mathbf{j})\,\text{km h}^{-1}$. At time 1200, the position vector of S relative to a fixed origin O is $(12\mathbf{i} + 4\mathbf{j})\,\text{km}$.

   (a) Find the bearing on which S is moving. **(2)**

   ....

   ....

   ....

   The ship is heading directly towards a submerged rock R. A radar tracking station calculates that, if S continues on the same course with the same speed, it will hit R at time 1600.

   (b) Find the position vector of R. **(2)**

   ....

   The tracking station warns the ship's captain of the situation. The captain maintains S on its course with the same speed until time 1400. He then changes course so that S moves due east at a constant speed of $6\,\text{km h}^{-1}$. Assuming that S continues to move with this new constant velocity, find

   (c) an expression for the position vector of the ship t hours after 1400 **(4)**

   ....

   ....

   (d) the time when S will be due north of R. **(2)**

   ....

   ....

   ....

   ....

   > When S is north of R, the $\mathbf{i}$ components of their position vectors will be the same.

Forces as vectors

Guided

1. A particle P of mass $5\,\text{kg}$ is moving under the action of a constant force $\mathbf{F}$ newtons. When $t = 0$, P has velocity $(4\mathbf{i} + 3\mathbf{j})\,\text{m s}^{-1}$ and at time $t = 5\,\text{s}$, P has velocity $(16\mathbf{i} - 6\mathbf{j})\,\text{m s}^{-1}$. Find

   (a) the acceleration of P in terms of $\mathbf{i}$ and $\mathbf{j}$ (2)

   $s = \dots\dots\quad u = \dots\dots\dots\quad v = \dots\dots\dots\quad a = \dots\dots\dots\quad t = \dots\dots$

   $16\underset{\sim}{\mathbf{i}} - 6\underset{\sim}{\mathbf{j}} = \dots\dots\dots\dots\dots$

   ....

   ....

   (b) the magnitude of $\mathbf{F}$ (4)   Use $\mathbf{F} = m\mathbf{a}$.

   $\underset{\sim}{\mathbf{F}} = 5(\dots\dots\dots\dots) = \dots\dots\dots\dots\dots$ If $\mathbf{F} = p\mathbf{i} + q\mathbf{j}$, then $|\mathbf{F}| = \sqrt{p^2 + q^2}$.

   $|\underset{\sim}{\mathbf{F}}| = \dots\dots\dots\dots$

   ....

   ....

2. A particle P of mass $0.6\,\text{kg}$ moves under the action of a single constant force $\mathbf{F}$ newtons. The acceleration of P is $(5\mathbf{i} + 12\mathbf{j})\,\text{m s}^{-2}$. Find

   (a) the angle between the acceleration and $\mathbf{i}$ (2)

   ....

   ....

   (b) the magnitude of $\mathbf{F}$. (3)

   ....

   ....

   At time t seconds the velocity of P is $\mathbf{v}\,\text{m s}^{-1}$. Given that when $t = 0$, $\mathbf{v} = 10\mathbf{i} - 5\mathbf{j}$

   (c) find the velocity of P when $t = 4$ (3)

   ....

   ....

3. A particle P of mass $3\,\text{kg}$ moves in a plane under the action of a single constant force $\mathbf{F}$ newtons. At time t seconds, the velocity of P is $\mathbf{v}\,\text{m s}^{-1}$. When $t = 0$, $\mathbf{v} = (-4\mathbf{i} + 6\mathbf{j})\,\text{m s}^{-1}$ and when $t = 3$, $\mathbf{v} = (2\mathbf{i} - 3\mathbf{j})\,\text{m s}^{-1}$.

   (a) Find the vector $\mathbf{F}$ in the form $a\mathbf{i} + b\mathbf{j}$. (5)

   ....

   ....

   ....

   (b) Find the value of t when $\mathbf{Q}$ is moving parallel to $\mathbf{i}$. (4)

   ....

   ....

   ....

Vectors and resultants

Guided

1. Two forces, $(3\mathbf{i} - 6\mathbf{j})\,\text{N}$ and $(p\mathbf{i} + q\mathbf{j})\,\text{N}$, act on a particle P of mass m kg. The resultant of the two forces is $\mathbf{R}$. Given that $\mathbf{R}$ acts in a direction which is parallel to the vector $(2\mathbf{i} - \mathbf{j})$

   (a) find the angle between $\mathbf{R}$ and the vector $\mathbf{j}$ **(3)**

   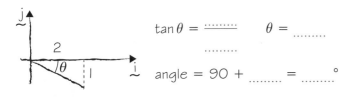

   $\tan\theta = \dfrac{\text{..........}}{\text{..........}}$ $\theta = \text{..........}$

   angle $= 90 + \text{..........} = \text{..........}°$

   > Draw a sketch to make sure you calculate the correct angle.

   (b) show that $p + 2q = 9$ **(4)**

   > To find the resultant, add the **i** components and the **j** components.

   ....

   ....

   Given also that $q = 2$ and that P moves with an acceleration of magnitude $6\sqrt{5}\,\text{m s}^{-2}$

   (c) find the value of m. **(7)**

   ....

   ....

   > Find $|\mathbf{R}|$ and use $|\mathbf{R}| = ma$ to find **m**.

2. A particle is acted upon by two forces $\mathbf{F_1}$ and $\mathbf{F_2}$, given by

   $\mathbf{F_1} = (2\mathbf{i} - 4\mathbf{j})\,\text{N}$

   $\mathbf{F_2} = (p\mathbf{i} + 2p\mathbf{j})\,\text{N}$, where p is a positive constant.

   (a) Find the angle between $\mathbf{F_2}$ and $\mathbf{i}$. **(2)**

   ....

   The resultant of $\mathbf{F_1}$ and $\mathbf{F_2}$ is $\mathbf{R}$. Given that $\mathbf{R}$ is parallel to $\mathbf{j}$

   (b) find the value of p. **(4)**   > If parallel to **j**, the **i** component is zero.

   ....

   ....

3. A particle P, of mass 3 kg, moves under the action of two constant forces $(4\mathbf{i} + 3\mathbf{j})\,\text{N}$ and $(5\mathbf{i} - 6\mathbf{j})\,\text{N}$.

   (a) Find, in the form $(a\mathbf{i} + b\mathbf{j})\,\text{N}$, the resultant force $\mathbf{F}$ acting on P. **(1)**

   ....

   (b) Find the acceleration of P, giving your answer as a vector. **(2)**

   ....

   The initial velocity of P is $(-3\mathbf{i} + 2\mathbf{j})\,\text{m s}^{-1}$.

   (c) Find, to 3 significant figures, the speed of P after 3 s. **(5)**

   ....

   ....

   ....

Modelling assumptions

> **Guided**

1. A block of wood *A* rests on a smooth inclined plane and is attached to one end of a light inextensible string. The string passes over a small smooth pulley *P* fixed at the edge of the plane. The other end of the string is attached to a ball *B* which hangs freely below the pulley. The system is released from rest with the string taut. In the resulting motion *A* and *B* are modelled as particles. State how you can use in your calculations that

   (a) the plane is smooth **(1)**

   If the plane is smooth ....

   > Think about the **friction**.

   (b) the string is light **(1)**

   ....

   > Think about the **weight**.

   (c) the string is inextensible **(1)**

   ....

   ....

   > Think about the **acceleration**.

   (d) the pulley is smooth **(1)**

   ....

   ....

   (e) *A* and *B* are modelled as particles. **(1)**

   ....

   ....

2. A ball is projected vertically upwards. After projection, the ball moves freely under gravity until it reaches the ground. In the resulting motion the ball is modelled as a particle. State how you can use in your calculations that the ball moves freely under gravity. **(1)**

   > If the ball moves **freely under gravity** you can ignore **air resistance**.

   ....

3. A heavy uniform steel girder *AB* has a load attached at *A* and one at *B*. The loaded girder hangs in equilibrium in a horizontal position, held by two vertical steel cables. The girder is modelled as a uniform rod, the loads as particles and the cables as light inextensible strings. State how you can use in your calculations that

   (a) the girder is uniform **(1)**

   ....

   > Think about where the **weight** of the girder acts.

   (b) the girder hangs in equilibrium **(1)**

   > Consider the **resultant force** on the girder.

   ....

   (c) the loads are modelled as particles **(1)**

   ....

   (d) the cables are modelled as light inextensible strings. **(1)**

   ....

You are the examiner!

Checking through your work is a key skill for AS maths. Have a look at pages 82 and 83 of the *Revision Guide*, then practise with these questions. There are full worked solutions on pages 170–171.

1. A ball is projected vertically upwards with a speed $u\,\text{m}\,\text{s}^{-1}$ from a point A which is 2.5 m above the ground. The ball moves freely under gravity until it reaches the ground. The greatest height attained by the ball is 28.9 m above A.

   > **Direction** is important in *suvat* questions. The ball is thrown **up** and gravity acts **down**. If your positive direction is up, then the final displacement, s, and the acceleration, a, are both negative.

   (a) Show that $u = 23.8$ **(3)**

   ....

   ....

   The ball reaches the ground T seconds after it has been projected from A.

   (b) Find, to 1 decimal place, the value of T. **(4)**

   ....

   ....

   ....

2. A particle P of mass 3.5 kg rests in equilibrium on a rough plane under the action of a force of magnitude X newtons acting up a line of greatest slope of the plane, as shown in the diagram. The plane is inclined at 15° to the horizontal. The coefficient of friction between P and the plane is 0.5. The particle is in limiting equilibrium and is on the point of moving up the plane.

   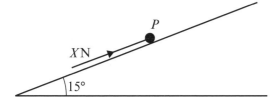

   > Draw all the forces which act on the particle on the diagram.

   > Remember to include all the forces when you are resolving. If a force acts at an angle, then it will have components parallel and perpendicular to the plane.

   Calculate

   (a) the normal reaction of the plane on P **(2)**

   ....

   ....

   > Resolve the forces **perpendicular** to the plane. The particle is in **equilibrium** so the **resultant force** in any direction is **zero**.

   (b) the value of X. **(4)**

   ....

   ....

   ....

   > Resolve the forces **parallel** to the plane. The parcel is **on the point of moving up** the plane so $F = \mu R$ and acts **down** the plane. The particle is in **equilibrium** so the **resultant force** in any direction is **zero**.

   The force of magnitude X newtons is now removed.

   (c) Show that P remains in equilibrium on the plane. **(4)**

   > P will remain in equilibrium if the component of weight down the plane is less than F_{max}.

   ....

   ....

You are the examiner!

Checking through your work is a key skill for AS maths. Have a look at pages 82 and 83 of the *Revision Guide*, then practise with these questions. There are full worked solutions on pages 170–171.

3. A particle P moves with constant acceleration $(3\mathbf{i} - 2\mathbf{j})\,\mathrm{m\,s^{-2}}$. At time t seconds, its velocity is $\mathbf{v}\,\mathrm{m\,s^{-1}}$. When $t = 0$, $\mathbf{v} = -3\mathbf{i} + 6\mathbf{j}$

(a) Find the value of t when P is moving parallel to the vector $\mathbf{i}$.   **(4)**

> When moving parallel to the vector $\mathbf{i}$, the $\mathbf{j}$ component of the velocity is zero.

....

....

....

....

(b) Find the speed of P when $t = 4$ **(3)**

> Check whether you are asked for the **velocity** or the **speed**. Speed is the **magnitude** of the velocity vector.

....

....

....

4. A particle P of mass $0.4\,\mathrm{kg}$ is moving with speed $u\,\mathrm{m\,s^{-1}}$ in a straight line on a smooth horizontal table. The particle P collides directly with a particle Q of mass $0.7\,\mathrm{kg}$, which is at rest on the table. Immediately after the particles collide, P has speed $3\,\mathrm{m\,s^{-1}}$ and Q has speed $6\,\mathrm{m\,s^{-1}}$. The direction of motion of P is reversed by the collision. Find

(a) the value of u **(4)**

> Momentum and impulse have direction as well as magnitude. Choose a positive direction (usually to the right) and stick to it.

....

....

....

....

....

(b) the magnitude of the impulse exerted by P on Q.   **(2)**

....

....

Immediately after the collision, a constant force of magnitude R newtons is applied to Q in the direction directly opposite to the direction of motion of Q. As a result Q is brought to rest in $1.5\,\mathrm{s}$.

(c) Find the value of R.   **(4)**

....

....

....

....

Mean

1. Over a period of weeks, 36 blackbirds were caught in a nature reserve.

    They were weighed and then released.

    Their masses, x grams, were such that $\sum x = 3362$

    (a) Find the mean of these data.   **(1)**

    ....

    ....

    The next five blackbirds caught weighed

    101.6 g, 104 g, 89.5 g, 94.1 g and 112.8 g.

    (b) Find the mean mass of all the birds caught so far.   **(2)**

    > There are now 41 blackbirds. Calculate the new total mass.

    ....

    ....

    ....

> **Guided**

2. These are the times taken, to the nearest minute, by a class of 32 students to travel to school on a particular day.

Time, t (minutes)	1–5	6–12	13–20	21–30
Frequency	6	11	7	8
Midpoint, x	3			25.5

    (a) Find the midpoints of the 6–12 minutes and the 13–20 minutes groups.   **(2)**

    ....

    ....

    (b) Estimate the mean of the journey times for the whole class.   **(2)**

    $$\bar{x} = \frac{\sum fx}{\sum f} = \frac{6 \times 3 + \rule{3cm}{0.4pt} + \rule{3cm}{0.4pt} + 8 \times 25.5}{32}$$

    $= \rule{6cm}{0.4pt}$

    ....

3. The table shows the distances some people travelled to work each day.

    Estimate the mean distance travelled.   **(4)**

Distance, d (km)	Frequency
$0 < d \leq 4$	9
$4 < d \leq 10$	17
$10 < d \leq 15$	33
$15 < d \leq 25$	24
$25 < d \leq 30$	11

    ....

    ....

    ....

    ....

    ....

Median and quartiles

Guided 1. The stem and leaf diagram shows the numbers of driving lessons taken by 23 people before they passed their test.

(a) Write down the modal number of lessons. **(1)**

....

(b) Find the values of the lower quartile, the median and the upper quartile. **(3)**

Number of lessons								Totals
0	8	9						(2)
1	1	1	3	4	7	8	9	(7)
2	0	0	3	6	7	8	8 8	(8)
3	2	3	3	4	5	5		(6)

Key | 1 | 8 means 18 lessons

$n = 23 \quad \frac{n}{2} = 11.5, \ Q_2 \text{ (median)} = 12\text{th value} = 23 \text{ lessons}$

....

....

....

....

2. Here are the ages of some people in a restaurant.

(a) Write down the modal age. **(1)**

....

(b) Find the values of the lower quartile, the median and the upper quartile. **(3)**

Age											Totals
1	6	7	8	8	8						(5)
2	0	0	1	4	5	5	6	7	7	9	(10)
3	4	5	7	8	9						(5)
4	1	2	2	4	7	8					(6)
5	2	2	5	7	9						(5)
6	6	6	8								(3)

Key | 1 | 7 means 17 years of age

....

....

....

....

> You have not been given the total number of people so you need to work this out first before finding the positions of the median and quartiles.

....

....

3. The stem and leaf diagram shows the heights, measured to the nearest centimetre, of some plants at a garden centre.

(a) Write down the modal height. **(1)**

....

(b) Find the values of the lower quartile, the median and the upper quartile.

Height															Totals
1	4	5	6	6	9										
2	2	2	3	3	4	5	6	6	7	7	7	7	9		
3	0	1	1	1	2	3	5	7	8	8	9				
4	1	2	3	4	5	5	7	9							
5	2	3	3	4	6	6	8								

Key | 1 | 6 means 16 cm

(3)

....

....

....

....

....

Linear interpolation

Guided 1. The table gives the weights, w (kg), of 270 items of baggage checked in on a flight at Gatwick airport.

Use interpolation to estimate the median, Q_2, of these items. Give your answer correct to 1 decimal place. **(2)**

Weight, w (kg)	Number of items
$0 < w < 10$	29
$10 \leqslant w < 15$	121
$15 \leqslant w < 22$	73
$22 \leqslant w < 30$	47

$\frac{n}{2} = 135$, so the median is $(135 - 29) = 106$ values

into the $10 \leqslant w < 15$ group.

This group is 5 kg wide so each member is worth $\frac{5}{121}$ kg.

$Q_2 = 10 + 106 \times \frac{5}{121}$ kg

    = ... kg

2. The table shows the speeds, v (mph), of 104 vehicles travelling along a country road.

Use interpolation to estimate the median, Q_2, the lower quartile, Q_1, and the upper quartile, Q_3, of these items.

Give your answers correct to 1 decimal place. **(4)**

Speed, v (mph)	Number of vehicles
$10 \leqslant v < 20$	6
$20 \leqslant v < 30$	12
$30 \leqslant v < 45$	29
$45 \leqslant v < 55$	23
$55 \leqslant v < 60$	15
$60 \leqslant v < 65$	19

....

....

....

....

....

....

....

Start by working out the values of $\frac{n}{4}, \frac{n}{2}$ and $\frac{3n}{4}$ to locate the positions of the median and the quartiles, then follow the same procedure as in Question 1.

3. The table shows the lengths of caterpillars, measured to the nearest millimetre.

Use interpolation to estimate the median, Q_2, the lower quartile, Q_1, and the upper quartile, Q_3, of these items.

Give your answers correct to 1 decimal place. **(4)**

Length (mm)	Frequency
1–10	16
11–25	33
26–45	38
46–65	27
66–75	10

....

....

....

....

....

....

....

Standard deviation 1

Guided **1.** The stem and leaf diagram shows the numbers of books read by 27 people in one year.

Given that $\sum x = 768$ and $\sum x^2 = 27\,872$, find the standard deviation of these data. **(2)**

> Don't forget: standard deviation = $\sqrt{\text{variance}}$

$\text{Variance} = \dfrac{\sum x^2}{n} - \left(\dfrac{\sum x}{n}\right)^2$

$\qquad = \dfrac{27\,872}{27} - \left(\dfrac{768}{27}\right)^2 =$ ....

Number of books							Totals
0	3	6	8				(3)
1	0	0	1	4	7	9	(6)
2	4	5	6	6	8		(5)
3	3	4	4	5	7	8	(6)
4	0	1	2	6			(4)
5	1	3	7				(3)

Key	3 $\vert$ 5 means 35 books

....

....

2. Here are the ages, x years, of some people in a restaurant.

Given that $\sum x^2 = 54\,431$, find the standard deviation of these data. **(3)**

> You need to work out $\sum x$ before you can use the formula for the variance.

Age											Totals
1	6	7	8	8	8						(5)
2	0	0	1	4	5	5	6	7	7	9	(10)
3	4	5	7	8	9						(5)
4	1	2	2	4	7	8					(6)
5	2	2	5	7	9						(5)
6	6	6	8								(3)

Key	1 $\vert$ 7 means 17 years of age

....

....

....

....

....

3. The stem and leaf diagram shows the numbers of letters received by some households in a week.

Find the standard deviation of the number of letters received by these households. **(5)**

Number of letters							
1	3	5	8	8	9		
2	0	0	1	4	6	6	7
3	1	1	2	4			

Key	2 $\vert$ 4 means 24 letters

....

....

....

....

....

....

....

....

Standard deviation 2

1. The table shows the times taken by 160 people to travel to work one morning.

Estimate the standard deviation of these data. **(5)**

Time, t (minutes)	Number of people	Midpoint
$0 \leqslant t < 10$	12	5
$10 \leqslant t < 15$	27	12.5
$15 \leqslant t < 30$	85	22.5
$30 \leqslant t < 50$	36	40

$$\sum f = 160$$

$$\sum fx = 12 \times 5 + 27 \times 12.5 + 85 \times 22.5 + 36 \times 40$$

$$= 3750$$

$$\sum fx^2 = 12 \times 5^2 + 27 \times 12.5^2 + \text{..................} + \text{..................}$$

$$= \text{..................}$$

$$\text{Variance} = \frac{\text{..................}}{160} - \left(\frac{3750}{160}\right)^2 = \text{..................}$$

> Start by finding the midpoint of each group – these will be the x values. Work out $\sum fx$ and $\sum fx^2$, then use the formula for the variance. Don't forget to square root to find the standard deviation.

....

....

2. The profits of 92 businesses are given in the table.

Estimate the standard deviation of these data. **(5)**

Profit, p (£ million)	Number of businesses
$1.0 \leqslant p < 2.0$	19
$2.0 \leqslant p < 2.8$	34
$2.8 \leqslant p < 3.6$	26
$3.6 \leqslant p < 5.0$	13

....

....

....

....

....

....

3. The table shows the lengths of some earthworms, measured to the nearest millimetre.

(a) Find the midpoints of the 30–46 and 66–75 groups. **(2)**

....

....

(b) Estimate the standard deviation of the lengths of these earthworms. **(3)**

Length (mm)	Frequency	Midpoint
11–29	16	20
30–46	36	
47–65	40	56
66–75	24	
76–100	10	88
101–120	14	110.5

[You may use $\sum fx^2 = 551\,493.5$]

....

....

....

....

Box plots and outliers

Guided 1. Carla recorded the ages of some people at a concert.
This table summarises her data.

An outlier is a value that is greater than Q_3 plus 1.25 times the interquartile range or less than Q_1 minus 1.25 times the interquartile range.

Draw a box plot to represent the data, indicating clearly any outliers. **(5)**

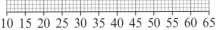

Two lowest values	11, 14
Lower quartile	28
Median	37
Upper quartile	40
Two highest values	53, 61

IQR = 40 − 28 = 12

1.25 × IQR = 1.25 × 12 = ...

Q_3 + ... = ...

....

....

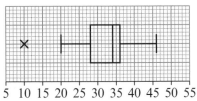

10 15 20 25 30 35 40 45 50 55 60 65

2. The box plot shows a summary of the marks gained by students in a test.
   (a) (i) Write down the mark that 75% of the students scored more than.
   (ii) State the name given to this mark. **(2)**

5 10 15 20 25 30 35 40 45 50 55
Mark

....

....

An outlier is a value greater than Q_3 plus 1.5 times the interquartile range or less than Q_1 minus 1.5 times the interquartile range.

(b) Show working to explain why 10 is an outlier. **(2)**

....

....

3. The stem and leaf diagram shows the numbers of cars parked in a town centre car park on different occasions.

An outlier is a value that is greater than Q_3 plus 1.5 times the interquartile range or less than Q_1 minus 1.5 times the interquartile range.

Draw a box plot to represent the data, indicating clearly any outliers. **(7)**

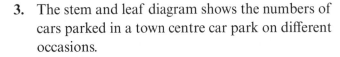

Number
of cars   Totals
0	7 9	(2)
1	5 8 9	(3)
2	6 6 6 7 7 8 8 9	(8)
3	0 1 1 2 6 7	(6)
4	3 8	(2)
5	3	(1)

Key | 1 | 9 means 19 cars

....

....

....

....

....

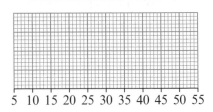

5 10 15 20 25 30 35 40 45 50 55

....

....

Histograms

1. The histogram shows information about how much time cars spent in a car park.

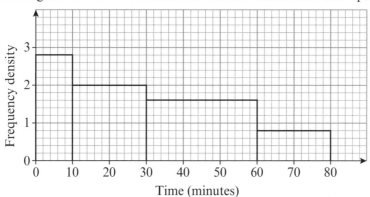

Time (minutes)

Frequency density × class width = frequency

Complete the table.   **(2)**

Frequency for $0 < t \le 10$ class = 2.8 × 10 = 28

Frequency for $10 < t \le 30$ class = 2 × ....

= ....

Time, t (minutes)	Number of cars
$0 < t \le 10$	28
$10 < t \le 30$	
$30 < t \le 60$	
$60 < t \le 80$	16

....

2. The speeds of cars along a stretch of road were recorded.

The histogram and the frequency table show the same information.

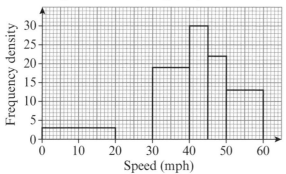

Speed (mph)

Speed, v (mph)	Number of cars
$0 < v \le 20$	60
$20 < v \le 30$	110
$30 < v \le 40$	190
$40 < v \le 45$	150
$45 < v \le 50$	
$50 < v \le 60$	130

(a) Complete the histogram and fill in the missing number in the frequency table.   **(2)**

....

....

(b) Estimate how many cars were travelling between 25 mph and 43 mph.   **(3)**

....

....

....

3. Poppy recorded the heights of 80 plant seedlings, to the nearest mm. This table shows her results.

Height (mm)	6–7	8–9	10–13	14–19
Frequency	8	32	24	18

A histogram was drawn and the bar representing the 8–9 class was 1 cm wide and 4 cm high.
Find the width and the height of the bar representing the 10–13 class.   **(3)**

....

....

Skewness

> **Guided**

1. This table shows some information for three sets of data.

   Describe the skewness of each set of data.

   Justify your answer. **(3)**

Data set	Lowest value	Lower quartile	Median	Upper quartile	Highest value
A	5	10	14	21	36
B	12	23	30	35	40
C	8	17	22	28	35

For data set A: $Q_2 - Q_1 = 14 - 10 = 4$

$\qquad\qquad\quad Q_3 - Q_2 = 21 - 14 = 7$

So, $Q_2 - Q_1 < Q_3 - Q_2$ and data set A is ....

....

....

....

2. This table shows the mean, median and standard deviation for three sets of data.

   One measure of skewness is $\dfrac{3(\text{mean} - \text{median})}{\text{standard deviation}}$

   Evaluate this measure and describe the skewness for each set of data. **(6)**

Data set	Mean	Median	Standard deviation
D	28.8	30.4	8.5
E	11.7	18.5	6.2
F	32.6	29.2	3.7

....

....

....

....

3. Here are the heights of 11 students, in centimetres, given to the nearest centimetre.

   168   154   166   174   150   154   161   168   159   175   157

   (a) Test the skewness of the data by working out the median and the quartiles. **(2)**

   ....

   ....

   ....

   (b) Given that $\sum x^2 = 290\,688$, work out a measure for the skewness of the data using

   $\qquad \dfrac{3(\text{mean} - \text{median})}{\text{standard deviation}}$

   and show how the result supports your answer to part (a). **(3)**

   ....

   ....

   ....

   ....

   ....

   ....

Comparing distributions

Guided 1. The box plots show the marks scored in an exam by the boys and the girls in a class.

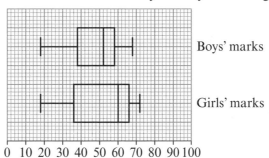

Boys' marks

Girls' marks

0 10 20 30 40 50 60 70 80 90 100

Compare and contrast the two sets of results. **(4)**

The median for the boys' marks (52) is less than the median for the girls' marks (60),

so the boys did less well overall.

The IQR for the boys was .... compared with .... for the girls.

....

....

> You also need to compare the skewness of the two data sets.

2. The back-to-back stem and leaf diagram shows the numbers of items of junk mail received each day in a three-week period by the residents in two villages, Duckford and Swanthorpe.

	Duckford	Number of items	Swanthorpe	
(1)	8	0	7 9	(2)
(3)	4 4 2	1	0 1 1 6 8 9	(6)
(5)	8 8 5 1 0	2	1 3 3 5 7 7	(6)
(4)	6 4 3 1	3	0 0 4 9	(4)
(6)	6 5 2 1 0 0	4	3 4	(2)
(2)	5 1	5	2	(1)

Key $2\,|\,1\,|\,0$ means 12 items in Duckford and 10 items in Swanthorpe

For Duckford

(a) find the values of the lower quartile, the median and the upper quartile **(3)**

....

(b) (i) find the mean of the number of items of junk mail

(ii) given that $\sum x^2 = 24\,548$, find the standard deviation of the data. **(4)**

....

....

Given that for Swanthorpe, the mean is 24.71, $Q_1 = 16$, $Q_2 = 23$, $Q_3 = 30$ and the standard deviation is 12.21

(c) compare the two distributions of items of junk mail. **(3)**

....

....

....

> Consider mean/median, spread and skewness.

Drawing Venn diagrams

Guided 1. 80 children were asked whether they had a cat, a dog or a rabbit as a pet.

31 of them had a cat
35 of them had a dog
18 of them had a rabbit
11 of them had a cat and a dog
7 of them had a cat and a rabbit
5 of them had a dog and a rabbit
2 of them had all three pets

(a) Draw a Venn diagram to represent this information. **(5)**

The 11 children who had a cat and a dog include the 2 children who had all three pets.

So 11 − 2 = 9 children had a cat and a dog but not a rabbit. This is $C \cap D \cap R'$.

....

....

....

....

....

....

(b) How many of the 80 children did not have a cat or a dog? **(1)**

....

2. 160 people were asked which of the countries France, Italy and Germany they had visited.

78 of them had been to France
43 of them had been to Italy
69 of them had been to Germany
21 of them had been to France and Italy
31 of them had been to France and Germany
20 of them had been to Italy and Germany
14 of them had been to all three countries

> Draw a rectangle to denote the whole sample space and draw three closed, intersecting circles for the three events, labelled F, I and G, inside the rectangle.

(a) Draw a Venn diagram to represent this information. **(5)**

....

....

....

....

....

....

....

(b) How many had been to exactly two of the three countries? **(1)**

....

Using Venn diagrams

Guided 1. The Venn diagram shows the numbers of students who take maths, English and history.

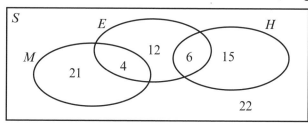

One of these students is selected at random.

(a) Show that the probability that the student takes only one of the subjects is $\frac{3}{5}$ **(2)**

The total number of students = 21 + 4 + 12 + 6 + 15 + 22 = 80

The number taking only one subject = 21 + 12 + ... = ...

So the probability is ....

(b) Find the probability that the student takes maths or English, or both.   **(2)**

....

2. For the events A and B, $P(A \cap B) = 0.23$, $P(A \cup B)' = 0.17$ and $P(B) = 0.54$

(a) Draw a Venn diagram to illustrate the complete
    sample space for events A and B.   **(4)**

> Instead of totals you write probabilities
> in the appropriate places on the Venn
> diagram. Remember that the total in
> the whole sample space must be 1.

(b) Write down the value of $P(A)$ and the value of $P(A' \cap B)$.   **(2)**

....

3. A survey showed that 68% of the people in a town shopped at Warners supermarket and
    46% shopped at Johnsons supermarket. 17% of the people in the town did not shop at either
    of these supermarkets.

(a) Draw a Venn diagram to represent this
    information.   **(4)**

> You can use percentages on a Venn diagram.
> Remember that the total in the whole sample
> space must be 100%.

A person from the town is chosen at random.

(b) Write down the probability that this person shops at either Warners or Johnsons,
    but not both.   **(2)**

....

Conditional probability

Guided

1. The Venn diagram shows the ice-cream flavours chosen by a group of 48 children at a party.

   The choices are vanilla (*V*), choc-chip (*C*) and toffee (*T*).

   A child is chosen at random.

   (a) Given that the child chooses choc-chip, find the probability that they also choose toffee. **(2)**

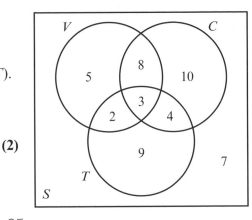

The number choosing choc-chip = 10 + 8 + 4 + 3 = 25

Of these 25, ... choose toffee, so the probability = $\dfrac{\text{............}}{25}$

   (b) Given that the child chooses vanilla or toffee, find the probability that they choose choc-chip. **(2)**

> The denominator of the probability fraction will be the total choosing vanilla or toffee or both of these.

....

....

....

2. The Venn diagram shows the sports played by a group of 80 students.

   The three most popular sports were tennis (*T*), golf (*G*) and basketball (*B*).

   A student is chosen at random.

   (a) Given that the student plays tennis, find the probability that they play all three sports. **(2)**

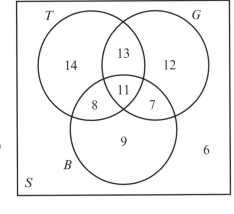

....

....

....

   (b) Given that the student plays at least two of the three sports, find the probability that they play golf and basketball. **(2)**

....

....

....

   (c) Given that the student does not play tennis, find the probability that they only play basketball. **(2)**

....

....

....

Probability formulae

Guided

1. Two events A and B are such that $P(A \cup B) = 0.85$, $P(A) = 0.7$ and $P(B) = 0.45$

Find the value of

(a) $P(A' \cap B')$ **(1)**

$P(A' \cap B') = 1 - P(A \cup B) = $ ....

(b) $P(A \cap B)$ **(2)**

$P(A \cap B) = P(A) + P(B) - P(A \cup B)$

$= 0.7 + 0.45 - 0.85$

$= $ ....

| Write in the probabilities as you work them out. |

(c) $P(A \cap B')$ **(1)**

....

(d) $P(A' \cup B)$ **(1)**

....

2. Matthew either walks or runs to the bus stop on his way to school.

The probability that he walks is 0.6

The probability that he catches the bus is 0.49

If he walks to the bus stop, the probability that he catches the bus is 0.35

Find the probability that

(a) Matthew walks to the bus stop and catches the bus   **(2)**

....

....

....

....

....

....

| Draw a Venn diagram representing the events W (for walking to the bus stop) and C (for catching the bus). Use the formula $P(C \mid W) = \dfrac{P(C \cap W)}{P(W)}$ to find $P(C \cap W)$. |

(b) Matthew runs to the bus stop but does not catch the bus   **(3)**

....

....

(c) Matthew catches the bus, given that he runs to the bus stop.   **(2)**

....

| On your Venn diagram, fill in the probabilities for $P(W \cap C')$, $P(C \cap W')$ and $P(W' \cap C')$. Remember that $P(\text{runs to the bus stop}) = P(W') = 1 - P(W)$. |

....

....

....

Had a go ☐   Nearly there ☐   Nailed it! ☐

Independent events

1. Given that $P(Q) = q$ and $P(R) = r$, express $P(Q \cup R)$ in terms of q and r when

    (a) Q and R are mutually exclusive **(1)**

    ....

    (b) Q and R are independent. **(1)**

    ....

> Guided

2. The Venn diagram shows the numbers of people who chose a chocolate biscuit (C), a wafer biscuit (W) or a ginger biscuit (G) from a box of biscuits.

    Determine whether choosing a chocolate biscuit and choosing a ginger biscuit are statistically independent. **(3)**

    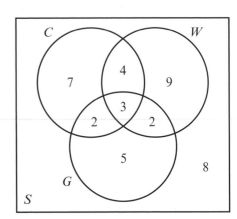

    Total number of people

    $$= 7 + 4 + 9 + 2 + 3 + 2 + 5 + 8 = \text{...........}$$

    $$P(C) = \frac{7 + 4 + 2 + 3}{\text{.........}} = \frac{16}{\text{.........}}$$

    $$P(G) = \frac{5 + 2 + \text{.........} + \text{.........}}{\text{.........}} =$$

    > Next, work out $P(C \cap G)$ and compare it to $P(C) \times P(G)$.

    ....

    ....

3. Two events A and B are independent.
    $P(B) = \frac{3}{8}$ and $P(A' \cap B') = \frac{1}{5}$
    Find

    > Remember that if A and B are independent, then A' and B' are also independent. Use the fact that $P(B') = 1 - P(B)$ and $P(A' \cap B') = P(A') \times P(B')$.

    (a) $P(A)$ **(4)**

    ....

    ....

    ....

    ....

    (b) $P(A \cap B)$ **(2)**

    ....

    ....

    (c) $P(A \cap B')$ **(2)**

    ....

    > If A and B are independent, then A and B' are also independent.

    ....

    (d) $P(A' \mid B)$. **(2)**

    ....

Tree diagrams

Guided 1. Marcus either gets up immediately when his alarm goes off or sleeps for a little while longer. The probability that he gets up immediately is 0.3

If he gets up immediately, the probability that he eats breakfast is 0.85 but if he sleeps for a little while longer, the probability that he eats breakfast is 0.45

(a) Draw a tree diagram to represent this information. **(2)**

0.85 — eats
0.3 — get up
...... — does not eat
0.45 — eats
...... — sleeps
...... — does not eat

(b) Find the probability that Marcus does not eat breakfast. **(3)**

> Remember to include both cases,
> P(gets up and does not eat) + P(sleeps and does not eat).

....

....

(c) Given that he does not eat breakfast, find the probability that he got up immediately when his alarm went off. **(3)**

....

....

....

2. When Keisha goes to a restaurant she always eats pizza or risotto for her main course and always eats apple pie or lemon tart for dessert.

The probability that she eats pizza is $\frac{3}{8}$ and the probability that she eats apple pie, given that she eats pizza, is $\frac{4}{5}$

The probability that she eats lemon tart, given that she eats risotto, is $\frac{2}{3}$

(a) Draw a tree diagram to represent this information. **(2)**

(b) Find the probability that Keisha eats either risotto or lemon tart, but not both. **(3)**

....

....

(c) Given that Keisha eats apple pie, find the probability that she ate pizza for her main course. **(4)**

....

....

....

Correlation

> **Guided**

1. The heights, h cm, and weights, w kg, of 12 people were measured.

The following summary statistics were calculated.

$$\sum h = 2067 \quad \sum w = 922 \quad \sum h^2 = 356\,899 \quad \sum w^2 = 72\,520 \quad \sum hw = 159\,555$$

(a) Calculate the value of S_{hh}, the value of S_{ww} and the value of S_{hw}.   **(4)**

$$S_{hh} = \sum h^2 - \frac{(\sum h)^2}{n} = 356\,899 - \frac{(2067)^2}{12} = \dots\dots\dots$$

....

....

....

....

....

(b) Calculate, to 3 significant figures, the product moment correlation coefficient between h and w.   **(2)**

$$r = \frac{S_{hw}}{\sqrt{S_{hh} \times S_{ww}}} = \dots\dots\dots$$

....

....

....

2. Ten students took two aptitude tests. The table shows their scores in each test.

Student	1	2	3	4	5	6	7	8	9	10
Verbal test (x)	67	81	56	51	86	65	48	74	67	69
Spatial test (y)	54	70	49	52	81	69	38	62	55	77

[You are given that $\sum x^2 = 45\,438 \quad \sum y^2 = 38\,485$ and $\sum xy = 41\,545$]

> First of all you need to calculate $\sum x$ and $\sum y$.

(a) Calculate the value of S_{xx}, the value of S_{yy} and the value of S_{xy}.   **(6)**

....

....

....

....

....

....

....

(b) Calculate, to 3 significant figures, the product moment correlation coefficient between x and y.   **(2)**

....

....

....

Understanding the PMCC

1. Here are three scatter diagrams for data sets A, B and C.

Set A 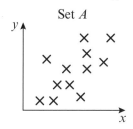 Set B 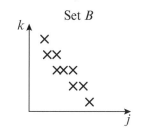 Set C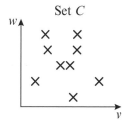

Here are five values of the product moment correlation coefficient.

0.92   −0.16   −0.91   −0.67   0.45

Select a value to match each data set, giving a reason for your choice. **(6)**

Set A: 0.45 because it shows positive correlation which is not very strong.

....

....

....

....

2. The number of hours of sunshine and the monthly rainfall were recorded over an eight-month period.

Month	Jan	Feb	Mar	Apr	May	June	July	Aug
Sunshine, x (hours)	85	91	98	110	105	120	130	124
Rainfall, y (cm)	4.8	4.6	5.3	5.7	4.2	3.1	3.4	2.7

[You are given that $\sum x = 863$ $\sum y = 33.8$ $\sum x^2 = 94\,911$ $\sum y^2 = 150.88$ $\sum xy = 3562.8$]

(a) Draw a scatter diagram for these data on the given axes. **(2)**

(b) Calculate the product moment correlation coefficient between x and y. **(6)**

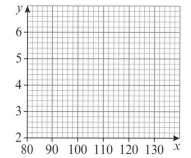

....

....

....

....

....

....

....

(c) Give an interpretation of your results. **(2)**

....

....

....

> Remember to refer to the context of the question. Writing 'positive correlation' or 'negative correlation' or 'no linear correlation' is not enough.

Regression lines

Guided 1. Eight students took tests in maths and science. The table shows their scores in each test.

Student	1	2	3	4	5	6	7	8
Maths score (x)	41	29	37	34	48	18	26	35
Science score (y)	43	25	40	30	38	23	25	28

[You are given that $\sum x = 268$ $\sum y = 252$ $S_{xx} = 598$ $S_{yy} = 418$ and $S_{xy} = 414$]

(a) Find the equation of the regression line of y on x in the form $y = a + bx$ **(5)**

$\bar{x} = \dfrac{268}{8} = 33.5$ and $\bar{y} = \dfrac{252}{8} =$ ....

$b = \dfrac{S_{xy}}{S_{xx}} = \dfrac{414}{598} =$ .... (3 s.f.) and $a = \bar{y} - b\bar{x} =$ .... − .... × 33.5 = ... (3 s.f.)

Equation is $y =$ ....

(b) State, with a reason, which variable is the independent variable.   **(2)**

....

The product moment correlation coefficient is 0.828 for these data.

(c) Explain why a regression model of the form $y = a + bx$ is supported for these data.   **(1)**

....

2. The load, x tonnes, and the fuel efficiency, y km per litre, were recorded for 10 lorries.

You are given that $S_{xx} = 20.62$ $\sum xy = 458.89$ $\sum x = 72$ $\sum y = 66.3$ $S_{yy} = 20.481$

(a) Find S_{xy}.   **(2)**

....

....

....

(b) Calculate the equation of the regression line of y on x in the form $y = a + bx$ **(3)**

....

....

....

> First, calculate the means for the x and y data. Then calculate b because you need it in your calculation for a. Be careful with your calculations because b is negative in this example.

....

....

....

(c) Find the product moment correlation coefficient and explain why a regression model of the form $y = a + bx$ is supported for these data.   **(3)**

....

....

....

....

Using regression lines

Guided 1. The journeys for a taxi company are represented by x miles and its fares are represented by £y.

This is a summary of the data for 20 journeys.

$$\sum x = 236 \qquad \sum y = 374 \qquad S_{xx} = 3136.4 \qquad S_{xy} = 4140.2$$

(a) Find the equation of the regression line of y on x in the form $y = a + bx$ **(5)**

$\bar{x} = \dfrac{236}{20} = 11.8$ and $\bar{y} = \dfrac{374}{20} = \dots\dots\dots$

$b = \dfrac{S_{xy}}{S_{xx}} = \dfrac{4140.2}{3136.4} = \dots\dots\dots$ (3 s.f.) and $a = \bar{y} - b\bar{x} = \dots\dots\dots$

(b) Give a practical interpretation of the values of a and b. **(2)**

2. A car manufacturer is testing the braking distance for a new model of car.

The table shows the braking distance, y metres, for different speeds, v km per hour, when the brakes were applied.

Speed, v (km/h)	30	50	60	80	90	100	110	130
Braking distance, y (metres)	25	65	78	145	155	215	235	332

[You are given that $S_{vv} = 7687.5 \quad S_{yy} = 72\,345.5 \quad S_{vy} = 23\,177.5$]

> You need to calculate the values of $\bar{v}$ and $\bar{y}$ before you can calculate the equation of the regression line. Work out the value of b first because you need it to find the value of a.

(a) Find the equation of the regression line of y on v in the form $y = a + bv$ **(5)**

(b) Use the equation of the regression line to estimate the braking distance for speeds of
   (i) 120 km/h   (ii) 150 km/h **(2)**

(c) Comment on the reliability of your estimates in part (b). **(2)**

(d) Find the product moment correlation coefficient for these data. **(2)**

(e) Is a linear regression model suitable for these data? Give a reason for your answer. **(1)**

Coding

Guided 1. The table shows the annual salaries, p (in £) of six office workers, along with the number of years (x) they have been working for a company.

Years, x	1	3	5	8	10	12
Salary, p (£)	14 000	15 200	16 600	19 000	20 900	23 000

The values of p are coded using $u = \dfrac{p - 14\,000}{1000}$

(a) Write down a table of values of x and u. **(2)**

x	1	3	5	8	10	12
u	0	1.2				9

(b) Calculate $\sum u$ and $\sum u^2$. **(2)**

....

....

(c) Find the mean and the standard deviation of the adjusted salaries (u). **(3)**

....

....

(d) Find the mean and the standard deviation of the original salaries (p). **(3)**

> Check what effect the coding has on the mean and the standard deviation of the coded data compared to the original data. The effect is not the same for both statistics.

....

....

2. Data was collected on the length of driving experience (x years) of eight car drivers and the times taken by them, t (seconds) to complete a circuit at a racing track.

The data for the times was coded using $u = \dfrac{t - 100}{5}$, and the following statistics were found.

$$\sum x = 58 \qquad \sum u = 84 \qquad S_{xx} = 143.5 \qquad S_{uu} = 250 \qquad S_{xu} = -185$$

(a) Find the equation of the regression line of u on x in the form $u = a + bx$ **(4)**

....

....

(b) Use your equation of the regression line to estimate the **actual** time taken by a driver with 6 years experience. **(3)**

> Remember that the regression line equation connects u (the coded value) and x. You need to calculate a value of t (the actual time).

....

....

(c) Find the product moment correlation coefficient between x and t. **(2)**

....

> It is the same as the one between x and u.

....

Random variables

> **Guided**

1. The discrete random variable X can take only the values 1, 2, 3 and 4

   X has probability function

   $$P(X = x) = \begin{cases} kx^2, & x = 1, 2, 3 \\ 3kx, & x = 4 \end{cases}$$

   where k is a constant.

   (a) Find the value of k and construct a table giving the probability distribution of X.   **(3)**

   $P(X = 1) = k \times 1^2 = k$, $P(X = 2) = k \times 2^2 = 4k$, $P(X = 3) = $ ...., $P(X = 4) = $ ....

   $k + 4k + $ .... $ + $ .... $ = 1$, giving $k = $ ....

x	1	2	3	4
$P(X = x)$				

   (b) Find $P(X < 3)$.   **(2)**

   ....

2. The discrete random variable Y can take only the values 1, 2, 3, 4 and 5

   Y has probability function $P(Y = y) = k(6y - y^2)$ for $y = 1, 2, 3, 4, 5$, where k is a constant.

   (a) Construct a table giving the probability distribution of Y.   **(3)**

   > Find the value of k first by calculating the probability for each event and using $\sum P(Y = y) = 1$.

   (b) Find $P(Y \geq 3)$.   **(2)**

   ....

3. The discrete random variable W has the probability distribution given by

w	−4	−1	0	1	3	6
$P(W = w)$	0.15	$2a$	a	0.05	0.1	$0.5a$

   where a is a constant.

   (a) Find the value of a.   **(2)**

   ....

   ....

   ....

   (b) Find $P(2W + 5 \geq 4)$.   **(2)**

   ....

   ....

   ....

   ....

Cumulative distribution

Guided 1. The discrete random variable X can take only the values 1, 2, 3 and 4

For these values the cumulative distribution function is defined by

$$F(x) = \frac{x^2 + k}{30}, \quad x = 1, 2, 3, 4$$

where k is a constant.

(a) Find the value of k.   (2)

> Remember that $P(X = 1) = F(1)$, $P(X = 2) = F(2) - F(1)$ and $P(X = 3) = F(3) - F(2)$. Check that all four probabilities add up to 1.

$F(4) = 1$ that is, $\dfrac{16 + k}{30} = 1$ so $16 + k =$ ...., $k =$ ....

(b) Find the probability distribution of X.   (4)

$P(X = 1) = F(1) = \dfrac{1 + k}{30} = \dfrac{\text{.......}}{30}$

$P(X = 2) = F(2) - F(1) =$

x	1	2	3	4
$P(X = x)$				

....

....

2. The discrete random variable Y can take only the values 1, 2 and 3

For these values the cumulative distribution function is defined by $F(y) = \dfrac{(2y + k)^2}{81}, \quad y = 1, 2, 3$

where k is a positive integer.

(a) Find the value of k.   (3)

....

(b) Find the probability distribution of Y.   (3)

....

....

....

3. The discrete random variable W can take only the values 1, 2, 3 and 4

The probability distribution of W is

w	1	2	3	4
$P(W = w)$	0.1	a	0.2	b

where a and b are constants.

The cumulative distribution function $F(w)$ of W is given in the following table.

w	1	2	3	4
$F(w)$	c	0.4	d	e

where c, d and e are constants.

(a) Find the values of a, b, c, d and e.   (6)

> Compare the probability distribution and the cumulative distribution to work out the missing values. Remember that $F(4) = 1$.

....

....

....

(b) Find $P(3W + 2 \leqslant 11)$.   (2)

....

....

Expectation and variance

> **Guided**

1. The discrete random variable X has the probability distribution

x	1	2	3	4	5
$P(X = x)$	0.3	0.05	0.2	0.35	0.1

(a) Find $E(X)$. **(2)**

$E(X) = 1 \times 0.3 + 2 \times 0.05 + 3 \times 0.2 + + = $

(b) Find $Var(X)$. **(3)**

$E(X^2) = 1^2 \times 0.3 + 2^2 \times 0.05 + + + = $

$Var(X) = E(X^2) - [E(X)]^2 = $

2. The discrete random variable Y has the probability function

$$P(Y = y) = \frac{2y^2 - 1}{56} \quad \text{for } y = 1, 2, 3, 4$$

(a) Find the probability distribution of Y. **(2)**

> Calculate $P(Y = 1)$, $P(Y = 2)$, $P(Y = 3)$ and $P(Y = 4)$, and put the outcomes and probabilities in a table.

....

....

....

(b) Find the exact value of $E(Y)$. **(3)**

> In this question, 'exact value' means your answer needs to be left as a fraction.

....

....

(c) Show that $Var(Y) = 0.596$ to 3 significant figures. **(4)**

....

....

....

3. The discrete random variable W has the probability distribution

w	−1	0	1	2	3
$P(W = w)$	0.15	0.2	a	b	0.1

(a) Given that $E(W) = 0.95$, write down two equations in a and b. **(3)**

....

> Remember that the sum of all the probabilities is 1.

....

....

(b) Find the value of a and the value of b. **(2)**

....

(c) Find the variance of W. **(3)**

....

....

Functions of random variables

1. The discrete random variable X is such that $E(X) = 4$ and $Var(X) = 1.5$

   Find

   (a) $E(2X + 3)$ **(2)**   (b) $Var(2X + 3)$ **(2)**   (c) $E(5 - 3X)$ **(2)**   (d) $Var(5 - 3X)$ **(2)**

   ....

   ....

   ....

▷ **Guided** ▷ 2. The discrete random variable Y has the probability distribution

y	−2	0	2	4	6
$P(Y = y)$	0.1	0.15	0.05	k	0.3

   (a) Find the value of k. **(2)**

   ....

   Find

   (b) $E(Y)$ **(2)**   (c) $Var(Y)$ **(3)**   (d) $E(5Y - 2)$ **(2)**   (e) $Var(5Y - 2)$ **(2)**

   (b) $E(Y) = (-2 \times 0.1) + (0 \times 0.15) + (2 \times 0.05) + (4 \times \text{........})+ (6 \times 0.3) = \text{..........}$

   (c) $E(Y^2) = (-2)^2 \times 0.1 + 0^2 \times 0.15 + 2^2 \times 0.05 + \text{................} + \text{................} = \text{............}$

        $Var(Y) = E(Y^2) - [E(Y)]^2 = \text{...}$

   ....

   ....

3. The discrete random variable W has the probability distribution

w	−2	−1	0	1	2	3
$P(W = w)$	0.2	0.1	0.3	0.05	0.15	0.2

   (a) Find $E(W)$. **(2)**

   ....

   ....

   (b) Find $Var(W)$. **(3)**

   ....

   ....

   $T = mW + 1$ and $E(T) = 1.9$

   (c) Find the value of m. **(3)**

   > $E(T) = E(mW + 1)$. Use the formula for $E(mW + 1)$ with the value for $E(W)$ found in part (a).

   ....

   ....

   (d) Find $Var(T)$. **(2)**

   ....

Normal distribution 1

1. Z is the standard normal distribution, $Z \sim N(0, 1^2)$.

    Use the normal distribution table to write down these probabilities.

    (a) $P(Z < 0.7)$ **(1)**   (b) $P(Z < 1.44)$ **(1)**   (c) $P(Z < 2.75)$ **(1)**

    ....

    ....

    ....

Guided 2. X is a normally distributed random variable with $X \sim N(5, 4^2)$.

    (a) Find $P(X < 7)$.   **(2)**

    When $x = 7$, $z = \dfrac{x - \mu}{\sigma} = \dfrac{7 - 5}{4} = 0.5$

    $P(X < 7) = P(Z < 0.5) = \ldots\ldots$

> For $P(Z < 0.5)$, look up $\Phi(0.5)$ in the normal distribution table. You can find a copy in the Mathematical Formulae and Statistical Tables booklet on the Edexcel website.

    ....

    (b) Find $P(X < 12.12)$.   **(2)**

    ....

    ....

    ....

    (c) Find $P(X < 6.48)$.   **(2)**

    ....

    ....

    ....

3. The heights of men are normally distributed with a mean of 176 cm and a standard deviation of 8 cm.

    (a) Find the probability that a man, chosen at random, is less than 182 cm tall.   **(2)**

    ....

    ....

    ....

    Two men are chosen at random.

    (b) Find the probability that both of them
        are less than 182 cm tall.   **(2)**

> These outcomes are independent of each other.

    ....

    ....

    (c) Find the probability that both of them
        are 182 cm or more in height.   **(2)**

> You have already found the probability that a man is less than 182 cm tall, so use P(a man is 182 cm or more) = 1 − P(a man is less than 182 cm).

    ....

    ....

    ....

Normal distribution 2

Guided   1. The weights of goldfish in a pet shop are normally distributed with mean 100 g and standard deviation 10 g.

A goldfish is selected at random.

Find the probability that it weighs

(a) more than 112 g   (3)

When $x = 112$, $z = \dfrac{x - \mu}{\sigma} = \dfrac{112 - 100}{10} = 1.2$

$P(X > 112) = P(Z > 1.2) = 1 - P(Z < 1.2) = 1 -$ .... = ...

(b) less than 96 g   (3)

When $x = 96$, $z = \dfrac{x - \mu}{\sigma} = \dfrac{96 - 100}{10} = -0.4$

$P(X < 96) = P(Z < -0.4) = P(Z > 0.4)$

$\qquad = 1 - P(\text{................})$

$\qquad = \text{................} = \text{................}$

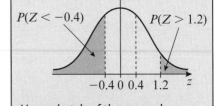

$P(Z < -0.4)$ $P(Z > 1.2)$

$-0.4\ 0\ 0.4\quad 1.2 \qquad z$

Use a sketch of the normal distribution curve to help you to solve problems using the symmetry of the curve.

(c) between 96 g and 112 g.   (3)

$P(96 < X < 112) = P(-0.4 < Z < 1.2)$

$\qquad = P(Z < 1.2) - P(Z < -0.4)$

$\qquad = \text{................}$

2. The lifetimes of a brand of electric light bulb are normally distributed with mean 1300 hours and standard deviation 120 hours. A light bulb is selected at random and tested by keeping it on continuously.

Find the probability that

(a) it has a lifetime of over 1540 hours   (3)

....

....

....

(b) it has a lifetime between 1222 and 1540 hours.   (4)

First, work out z when $x = 1222$, then find $P(X < 1222)$.

....

....

....

....

....

....

Two light bulbs are selected at random.

(c) Find the probability that they both last between 1222 and 1540 hours.   (2)

....

Finding unknown values

> **Guided**

1. A random variable X is normally distributed with mean 80 and standard deviation 10

   (a) Find a such that $P(X < a) = 0.305$ **(4)**

   $P(X < a) = P\left(Z < \dfrac{a - 80}{10}\right) = 0.305$

   $1 - 0.305 = \text{..........}$ and $P(Z < \text{..........}) = \text{..........}$

   So $P(Z < - \text{..........}) = 0.305$

   $\dfrac{a - 80}{10} = - \text{..........}$, giving $a = \text{..........}$

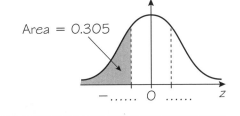

Area = 0.305

   (b) Find b such that $P(X > b) = 0.102$ **(4)**

> Draw a sketch of the normal distribution curve to help you to solve this. Use the symmetry of the curve. Remember to use the expression for the standardised normal variable.

   ....

   ....

   ....

   ....

   ....

2. The length of the life of a car tyre, L, is normally distributed with mean 18 000 miles and standard deviation 1600 miles.

   (a) Find the upper quartile of this distribution. **(3)**

   > Use $z = 0.67$ since $\Phi(0.67) = 0.7486$ and this is the closest value to 0.75.

   ....

   ....

   ....

   ....

   (b) Find the lower quartile of this distribution. **(2)**

   ....

   ....

   ....

3. The heights, H, of 18-year-old girls can be modelled by a normal distribution with mean 163 cm and standard deviation 6 cm.

   Find the range of heights that includes the middle 70% of 18-year-old girls.

   Give your answers to 1 decimal place. **(5)**

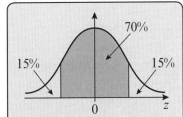

   > Use the fact that there will be 15% (probability = 0.15) in each end area. Use the percentage points table to find the appropriate z value.

   ....

   ....

   ....

   ....

   ....

   ....

Finding μ and σ

Guided   1.   Tins of soup are filled automatically by a machine. The tins are meant to contain 440 ml of soup.

The amounts of soup in a tin are normally distributed with mean 452 ml.

The law states that 99% of the tins of soup the company makes must contain at least 440 ml, as advertised.

Find the standard deviation of the amount of soup in a tin if the company obeys the law.   **(5)**

$$P(X > 440) = P\left(Z > \frac{440 - 452}{\sigma}\right) = 0.99$$

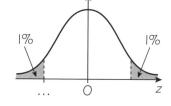

$$P(Z > \text{..................}) = 0.99 \text{ (using the percentage points table)}$$

$$\frac{440 - 452}{\sigma} = -\text{....................}$$

....

....

2. X is a normally distributed random variable with mean μ and standard deviation σ.

$P(X > 20.6) = 0.4$

(a) Show that $\mu = 20.6 - 0.2533\sigma$ **(3)** | Use the percentage points table: $P(Z > 0.2533) = 0.4$

....

....

....

....

....

....

You are also given that $P(X < 13.2) = 0.15$

(b) Form a second equation in μ and σ and hence find the values of the mean and standard deviation of X.   **(5)**

....

.... | The percentage points table tells you that $P(Z > 1.0364) = 0.15$. Be careful because the z-value needs to be negative.

....

....

....

....

....

....

....

....

....

....

You are the examiner!

Checking through your work is a key skill for AS maths. Have a look at pages 112 and 113 of the *Revision Guide*, then practise with these questions. There are full worked solutions on page 175.

1. The discrete random variable X can take only the values 2, 3 and 4

   For these values, the cumulative distribution function is defined by

   $$F(x) = \frac{x^2 + k}{36} \qquad x = 2, 3, 4$$

   (a) Find the value of k. **(2)**

   > This is the cumulative distribution function so $F(4) = 1$.

   ....

   ....

   (b) Find the probability distribution of X. **(3)**

   ....

   > Put the outcomes and probabilities in a table and check that the total of the probabilities is 1.

   ....

   ....

   Given that $E(X) = \frac{91}{36}$ and $Var(X) = \frac{827}{1296}$

   (c) Find the exact value of $E(3X + 5)$. **(2)**

   ....

   ....

   (d) Find the exact value of $Var(3X + 5)$. **(2)**

   ....

2. A case contained 150 oranges. The case was opened and each orange was weighed to the nearest gram. The weights are recorded in this table.

Weight (g)	50–69	70–99	100–119	120–159	160–219
Frequency	15	21	30	48	36

   > In a histogram the area is proportional to the frequency, not equal to it. Use proportion (or frequency density) to work out the height.

   A histogram was drawn and the 70–99 group was represented by a rectangle 3 cm wide and 2.8 cm high.

   (a) Calculate the width and height of the rectangle representing the 120–159 group. **(3)**

   > Be careful with class boundaries. The 70–99 group starts at 69.5 and has class width 99.5 – 69.5 = 30.

   ....

   ....

   ....

   ....

   (b) Use linear interpolation to estimate the median weight of an orange. **(4)**

   ....

   ....

   > The median is the 75th value. First, locate the group that contains the median.

   ....

   ....

You are the examiner!

Checking through your work is a key skill for AS maths. Have a look at pages 112 and 113 of the *Revision Guide*, then practise with these questions. There are full worked solutions on page 175.

3. Some people were playing a new computer game. They recorded their best points score, p, and the number of times they had played the game, t. The data for the points score was coded using $x = \dfrac{p - 2500}{100}$, and the following statistics were calculated.

    $S_{tt} = 462$ $S_{tx} = 516$ $S_{xx} = 641$ $\bar{t} = 16$ $\bar{x} = 15$

    (a) Show that the equation of the regression line of x on t is

    $$x = -2.87 + 1.12t \qquad \textbf{(4)}$$

    > Take care when working out b (the regression coefficient). The order of the variables is important so make sure you use the correct denominator.

    ....

    ....

    ....

    ....

    ....

    ....

    ....

    ....

    ....

    ....

    (b) Using your regression line, estimate the best points score of someone who had played the game 20 times. **(3)**

    > Remember that the regression line equation connects x (the coded value) and t. You need to calculate a value of p (the actual best points score).

    ....

    ....

    ....

    ....

    ....

    ....

Flow charts

1. The flow chart describes an algorithm.

(a) Use the flow chart with
$A = 6$ and $B = 10$ and
complete the table. **(4)**

A	B	C	D	Output
6	10	0	0	
		6	10	
		12		

> The values of C and D keep
> changing, so keep track of your
> working. The only output value
> occurs at the end of the process.

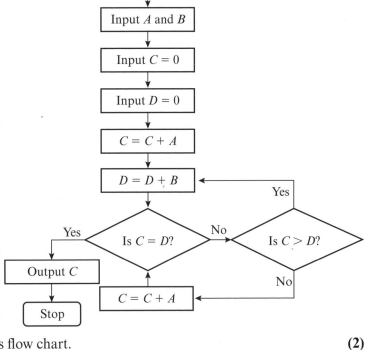

(b) Explain what is achieved by this flow chart. **(2)**

....

(c) Given that $A = kB$ for some positive integer k, write down the output of the flow chart. **(1)**

....

2. Here is a flow chart.

(a) Use the flow chart with $A = 1$, $B = -10$
and $C = 24$ and complete the table. **(5)**

A	B	C	N	X	Y	Output
1	-10	24				

(b) Explain what this flow chart achieves. **(2)**

....

....

(c) Why is the question 'Is $N = 2$?'
included in the flow chart? **(1)**

....

> There is more
> than one output.

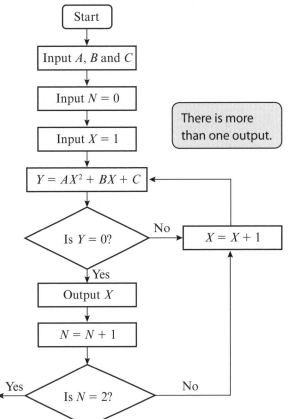

Bubble sort

> **Guided**

1. (a) Use a bubble sort to write this list of numbers in **descending** order.

11   4   9   12   10

You only need to write down the final result of each pass. **(4)**

	II	4	9	12	10	
	II	9	4	12	10	(swap 4 and 9)
	II	9	12	4	10	(swap 4 and 12)
After 1st pass	II	9	12	10	4	(swap 4 and 10)
						end of first pass
After 2nd pass	II	12	....			

> The whole of the first pass has been shown as an example.

> Keep going until there are no swaps in a pass.

....

....

(b) How many passes were needed? **(1)**

....

2. Use a bubble sort to write these letters in alphabetical order.

D   B   F   E   G   B

You only need to write down the final result of each pass. **(4)**

....

....

....

....

....

....

3. Here are the test scores of eight students.

79   26   45   50   81   32   45   63

Perform a bubble sort to list them in **descending** order.
You only need to write down the final result of each pass. **(4)**

....

....

....

....

....

....

....

Quick sort

> **Guided**

1. Use a quick sort to put this list of numbers in **ascending** order.

   4   9   2   7   6   1   3   8   5   (5)

   4   9   2   7   ⑥   1   3   8   5

   4   2   ①   3   5   ⑥   9   ⑦   8

   ①   4   2   ③   5   ⑥   ....

   > 6 is the first pivot because it is the fifth element in a list of nine elements. Colour code or highlight the pivots: in this example, a grey circle shows a new pivot and a plain circle shows a used pivot. Colour in any elements that are on their own as you go along.

   ....
   ....
   ....
   ....

2. Use a quick sort to put these names in alphabetical order.

   Lily   Grace   Susan   Ann   Helen   Beth   Katy   Ruby   (5)

   > There are eight elements, so you need to round up; the one to the right of the middle is the first pivot (Helen).

   > If you mark the pivots, there will always be one element in the last line that is a new pivot – all the others will have been marked.

   ....
   ....
   ....
   ....
   ....
   ....
   ....

3. Use a quick sort to put this list of numbers in **descending** order.

   > There are 10 elements, so the sixth one (37) is the first pivot.

   46   32   58   75   40   37   29   81   16   55   (5)

   ....
   ....
   ....
   ....
   ....
   ....
   ....

Binary search

Guided 1. Here is a list of some countries, in alphabetical order.

Australia	Belgium	Chile	Ecuador
Greece	Italy	Latvia	Norway
Poland	Spain	Turkey	Wales

Use the binary search algorithm to locate the country Chile.   **(4)**

> Writing the list horizontally saves a bit of space. Here the first pivot is the seventh element.

> Write out the new list after each iteration. Don't stop when you reach one item – select it as a pivot and state that it has been found.

A   B   C   E   G   I   Ⓛ   N̶   P̶   S̶   T̶   W̶

A   B   C   Ⓔ   G̶   I̶

....
....

2. Here is a list of some of the Premier League football teams in England, in alphabetical order.

Arsenal	Chelsea	Everton
Fulham	Hull City	Liverpool
Manchester United	Newcastle United	Sunderland
Tottenham Hotspur	West Ham United	

Use the binary search algorithm to locate Tottenham Hotspur.   **(4)**

....
....
....
....
....

3. Here is a list of eight years.

1946   1215   1914   2001   1812   1666   1492   1966

(a) Use a quick sort to put these years into chronological order.   **(5)**

....
....
....
....
....

(b) Use the binary search algorithm to locate the year 1492.   **(4)**

....
....
....

Bin packing 1

Guided 1. Boxes of the following heights, in centimetres, are to be packed into crates 1 metre high.

50   85   68   44   36   60   27

(a) Obtain a lower bound for the number of crates needed. **(2)**

50 + 85 + 68 + 44 + 36 + 60 + 27 = 370

370 ÷ .... = ... so .... crates is the lower bound.

(b) Use the first-fit bin-packing algorithm to find out how many crates are needed. **(4)**

Crate 1   50   ....

Crate 2   85   ....

> Keep a check on how much space is left in each crate as you select each item.

....

....

2. Bags containing the following amounts, in litres, are to be loaded into bins of capacity 300 litres.

175   206   80   142   125   97   112   64   70

(a) Obtain a lower bound for the number of bins needed. **(2)**

....

(b) Use the first-fit bin-packing algorithm to find out how many bins are needed. **(4)**

....

....

....

....

3. Items of the following heights, in metres, are loaded onto trolleys 1.6 metres high.

0.9   1.2   0.6   0.3   1.3   0.8   1.4   1.1

(a) Obtain a lower bound for the number of trolleys needed. **(2)**

....

(b) Use the first-fit bin-packing algorithm to find out how many trolleys are needed. **(4)**

....

....

....

....

....

(c) What do you notice about the amount of wasted space?
    Is the solution optimal? Explain your answer. **(3)**

....

....

Bin packing 2

Guided **1.** The weights of some packages, in kilograms, are listed in **descending** order.

60   58   47   42   29   25   18   13   12   10

(a) Use the first-fit decreasing bin-packing algorithm to determine how these packages can be put into bins capable of taking 80 kilograms. **(3)**

Bin 1   60   ....

Bin 2   58   ....

Bin 3   47   ....

> Keep a check on how much space is left in each bin as you select each item.

....

....

(b) Use the full bins algorithm to find an optimal solution that uses the minimum number of bins and explain why your solution is optimal. **(4)**

....

....

....

....

> Work out the lower bound first, then look for groups of numbers that add up to 80 and fill the other bins using the first-fit algorithm.

....

....

2. Boxes are being placed on shelves that are 3 metres long.
The boxes have the following lengths, in metres and are listed in **descending** order.

2.7   2.5   1.5   1.2   1.0   0.9   0.8   0.6

(a) Use the first-fit decreasing bin-packing algorithm on your ordered list to find how many 3-metre shelves are needed. How much shelf space is still empty? **(4)**

....

....

....

....

....

....

(b) Use the full bins algorithm to find an optimal solution that uses the minimum number of shelves and explain why your solution is optimal. How much shelf space is still empty? **(4)**

....

....

....

....

....

Graphs

Guided   **1.**   (a)   Find the degree of each vertex in this graph.   (2)

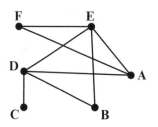

Vertex	A	B	C	D	E	F
Degree	3	2				

(b)   Draw a graph with five vertices with the number of degrees as shown in this table.

Vertex	P	Q	R	S	T
Degree	2	3	4	2	3

(3)

Guided   **2.**   For this graph

     (a)   (i)   is **P** connected to **Q**?

Yes, path PRVQ

         (ii)   is **R** connected to **U**?   (2)

....

     (b)   Write down all the paths from **Q** to **T**.   (2)

....

> A path is a route through a graph from one vertex to another. Vertices are connected if there is a path between them.

3.   Here is a graph.

     (a)   Write down the degree of vertex **A**.   (1)

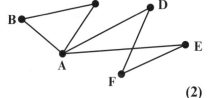

....

     (b)   Identify   (i)   a path from **C** to **F**   (ii)   a cycle.   (2)

....

     (c)   Identify whether the following are paths. If they are not paths, explain why.
         (i)   **ADEF**   (ii)   **FDACB**   (iii)   **EACBAD**   (6)

....

....

     (d)   Sketch   (i)   a spanning tree for this graph
               (ii)   a complete subgraph of this graph.   (3)

> A spanning tree is a subgraph of a graph which includes all the vertices and is also a tree.

Drawing networks

> **Guided** 1. Represent each of these graphs with a distance matrix.

(a)

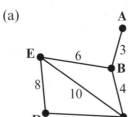

(2)

	A	B	C	D	E
A	–	3	–	–	–
B	3	–	4		
C	–				
D	–				
E	–			8	

(b)

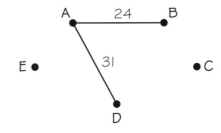

(2)

	P	Q	R	S	T
P	–	11			
Q	11	–			13
R					
S					
T					

> **Guided** 2. The table shows the distances, in kilometres, of a network of roads between five towns **A**, **B**, **C**, **D** and **E**.

	A	B	C	D	E
A	–	24	–	31	20
B	24	–	17	–	–
C	–	17	–	11	14
D	31	–	11	–	9
E	20	–	14	9	–

A ——— 24 ——— B

E •   31   • C

D

Complete the weighted network diagram for this table.   **(4)**

3. (a) Draw a weighted network diagram for this distance matrix.   **(4)**

	A	B	C	D	E	F
A	–	14	–	–	17	9
B	14	–	15	–	20	–
C	–	15	–	–	18	–
D	–	–	–	–	–	25
E	17	20	18	–	–	11
F	9	–	–	25	11	–

> Draw the network in the space to the right of the table.

(b) Sketch a spanning tree for this network.   **(3)**

> A spanning tree: is a subgraph; includes all the vertices; is a tree.

(c) Write down the total weight of your spanning tree.   **(1)**

....

Kruskal's algorithm

Guided

1. (a) Use Kruskal's algorithm to find a minimum spanning tree for this network. List the arcs in the order you consider them, stating whether or not they are to be included. **(3)**

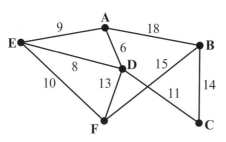 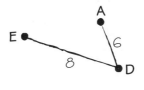

AE would form a cycle with the two edges already included.

AD (6) ✓   DE (8) ✓   AE (9) ✗ ....

(b) Draw the minimum spanning tree. **(2)**

You can draw the minimum spanning tree as you select the arcs. Remember to show the edges you include and the edges you reject in the right order.

(c) Write down the weight of the minimum spanning tree. .... **(1)**

2. (a) Use Kruskal's algorithm to find a minimum connector for this network. **(4)**

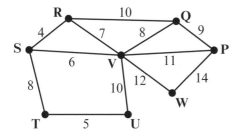

Draw the minimum connector in the space to the right of the network.

....

....

(b) Write down the total weight of the minimum connector. .... **(1)**

3. (a) Draw a weighted network diagram for this distance matrix. **(3)**

	A	B	C	D	E	F
A	–	–	–	–	20	–
B	–	–	16	25	–	35
C	–	16	–	–	18	–
D	–	25	–	–	30	40
E	20	–	18	30	–	–
F	–	35	–	40	–	–

(b) Use Kruskal's algorithm to find a minimum spanning tree for your network. List the arcs in the order you consider them, stating whether or not they are to be included. **(4)**

....

....

....

(c) Write down the weight of the minimum spanning tree. .... **(1)**

Prim's algorithm

> **Guided**

1. Here is a network.

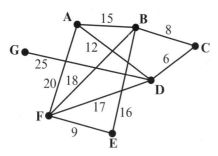

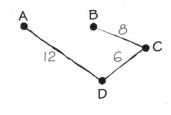

   (a) Use Prim's algorithm, starting from **D**, to find a minimum spanning tree. Draw your minimum spanning tree and clearly label the arcs in the order they are selected. **(4)**

   > Remember to choose the arc of least weight each time.

   DC (6)   CB (8)   DA (12) ....

   (b) Write down the weight of your minimum spanning tree. .... **(1)**

> **Guided**

2. In this matrix there are five locations, **P**, **Q**, **R**, **S** and **T**. The numbers represent the travelling times, in minutes, to drive between them.

	P	Q	R	S	T
P	–	25	–	30	12
Q	25	–	35	24	20
R	–	35	–	18	40
S	30	24	18	–	32
T	12	20	40	32	–

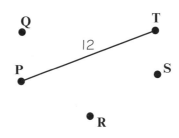

   Use Prim's algorithm, starting from **P**, to find a minimum spanning tree.
   List the order in which you select the arcs and draw the tree in the space above. **(4)**

   PT (12) ....

3. This matrix represents the length, in kilometres, of the water mains connecting seven towns.

	H	I	J	K	L	M	N
H	–	25	–	15	–	20	–
I	25	–	18	13	–	–	–
J	–	18	–	–	28	–	22
K	15	13	–	–	–	–	14
L	–	–	28	–	–	9	11
M	20	–	–	–	9	–	12
N	–	–	22	14	11	12	–

   Use Prim's algorithm, starting from **H**, to draw the minimum spanning tree and state the weight of the minimum spanning tree. List the order in which you select the arcs. **(5)**

   ....

Dijkstra's algorithm

Guided   **1.** The network represents the times, in minutes, to walk between nine places on a woodland walk.

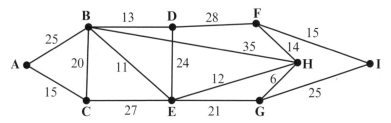

> List the working values in the correct order. Do not cross out any values, and write the new working value next to the old one.

> Trace the path backwards. Include an arc if arc length = difference in final values of end vertices.

Use Dijkstra's algorithm to work out the shortest time to walk from **A** to **I**. State your shortest route and the time taken.   **(6)**

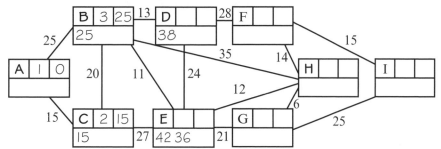

2. The numbers on this network represent the distances, in kilometres, between 11 towns.

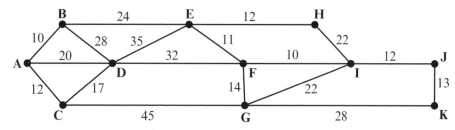

(a) Harry wants to go from **A** to **K** in his car. He can average a speed of 40 km per hour. Use Dijkstra's algorithm on the grid below to work out the shortest time the journey should take. Write down the route he should take.   **(6)**

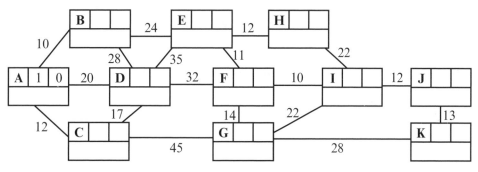

(b) The road from **J** to **K** is blocked. What route should he now take and how much longer will the journey take?   **(3)**

Route inspection

> **Guided**

1. The network shows roads linking towns **A** to **H**. The distances given are in kilometres.

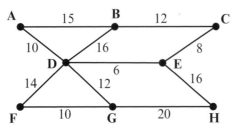

The total weight of the network is 139 km.

Mark needs to visit all the towns. He wishes to minimise the distance he travels.
Use the route inspection algorithm to find which arcs need to be repeated, making your method and working clear. State the length of the route. **(6)**

Degree of vertices: A 2   B 3   C 2   D 5   E 3   F 2   G 3   H 2

Odd vertices: B, D, E, G   Possible pairings: BD + EG (through D) = 16 + 18 = 34

> Start by finding the odd vertices and write down all the possible pairings.

BE + ...

....

Link vertices .... and .... by repeating arcs ....

Link ....

Length of route = ...

2. Here is a network.

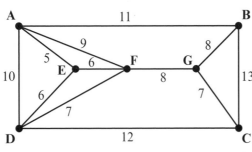

The total weight of the network is 102.

(a) Identify the odd vertices in this network. **(2)**

....

....

(b) Write down all possible pairings of odd vertices and find which arcs must be repeated. **(3)**

....

....

....

....

....

(c) Find a minimum inspection route for the network, starting and ending at **D**, and state its length. **(3)**

> Your route will visit some of the vertices more than once. Check that your final route has the **minimum** length.

....

....

Activity networks

> **Guided** 1. (a) In the activity network below, explain the significance of the dotted line from event 2 to event 4 and the dotted line from event 3 to event 4. **(2)**

A dotted line is a dummy activity. The one from event 2 to event 4 shows that activity E

depends on activity A as well as on activity B. The one from event 3 to ....

....

(b) Complete the precedence table for this activity network. **(2)**

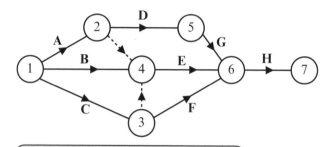

> Remember that you only need to fill in the immediately preceding activities.

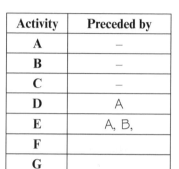

Activity	Preceded by
A	–
B	–
C	–
D	A
E	A, B,
F	
G	
H	

2. Complete the precedence table for this activity network. **(3)**

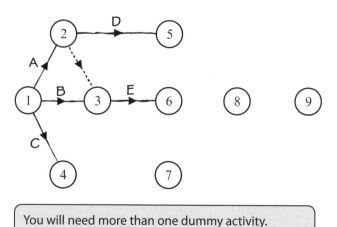

> Be careful with activities **C**, **D** and **G**. The dummy activities mean that all of them will depend on more than one preceding activity.

Activity	Preceded by
A	–
B	–
C	
D	
E	
F	
G	

> **Guided** 3. This precedence table contains 10 activities.
> Complete the drawing of the network that illustrates this information. **(4)**

> You will need more than one dummy activity.

Activity	Preceded by
A	–
B	–
C	–
D	A
E	A, B
F	C, D
G	C
H	E
I	E, G
J	F, H, I

126

Early and late times

Guided > 1. Here is a network of 10 activities.
The time taken, in minutes, to complete each activity is shown in brackets. Complete the diagram to show the early and late times for this network. **(4)**

> Dummies have a weight of 0.

> When going forwards, look to see how many activities **go into** a node and choose the largest value of your additions.

> When going backwards, look to see how many activities **come from** a node and choose the smallest value of your subtractions.

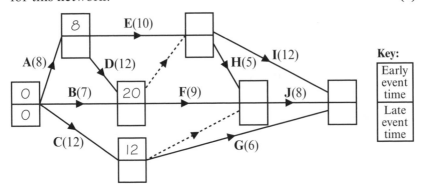

2. This network represents the 10 tasks needed in a manufacturing process.
The time taken, in minutes, to complete each task is shown in brackets.

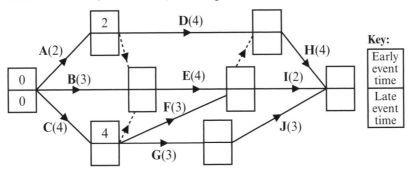

Complete the diagram to show the early and late times for each stage of the process. **(4)**

3. The time taken, in hours, for each stage of a project is shown in brackets on each stage of the activity network.

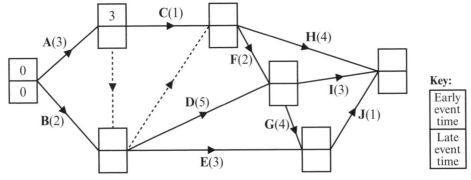

Complete the diagram to show the early and late times for each stage of the project. **(4)**

Critical paths

Guided 1. Here is an activity network.

(a) Complete the diagram to show the early and late times. **(3)**

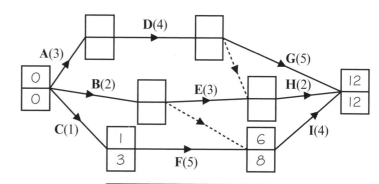

(b) Identify the critical path. **(3)**

....

> The critical path goes from source node to sink node and contains **only** the critical activities.

(c) Calculate the total float on activities **E**, **F** and **H**. **(3)**

For F, total float = 8 − 1 − 5
            = 2

Activity	E	F	H
Total float		2	

....

....

> Total float
> = latest end time − earliest start time − duration

2. The activity network represents a manufacturing process. The times, in minutes, for each task are shown in brackets on the arcs.

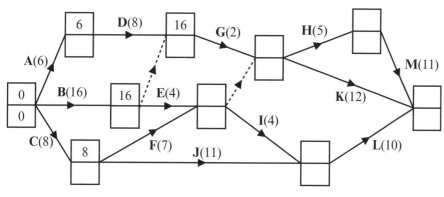

(a) Complete the diagram to show the early and late times for this network. **(5)**

(b) Identify the critical path. **(1)**

....

(c) Calculate the total float on activities **A**, **F** and **J**. **(3)**

....

....

....

(d) Explain the significance of the total float for activity **A**. **(1)**

....

> The total float on an activity is the maximum length of time the activity can be delayed without delaying the whole project.

....

Gantt charts

1. Here is an activity network.

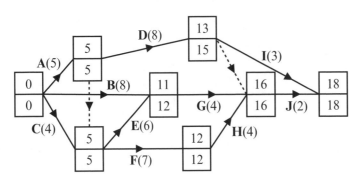

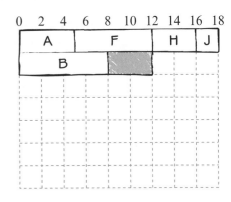

(a) Identify the critical path. A, F, H, J   **(2)**

(b) Calculate the total float for each activity.   **(3)**

For B, total float = 12 − 0 − 8 = 4

Activity	B	C	D	E	G	I
Total float	4					

(c) Draw a Gantt (cascade) chart on the
     grid next to the network.   **(4)**

> Remember to shade in the float for each non-critical
> activity. Make sure you include every activity.

2. The network shows the activities involved in a construction project, where the times shown are
    in months.

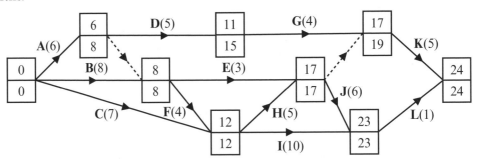

(a) Identify the critical path. .... **(2)**

(b) Draw a Gantt chart on this grid.   **(7)**

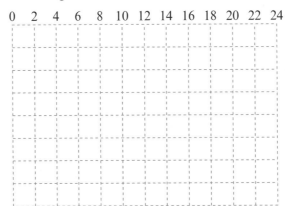

129

Scheduling

Guided 1. This Gantt chart is for a project where the times are in days.

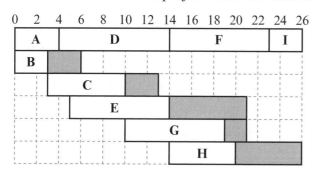

Lower = sum of all ÷ length of
bound activity times critical path.
Remember to round appropriately.

(a) Calculate a lower bound for the number of workers needed to finish the project in the minimum time. **(2)**

Lower bound = 60 ÷ 26 = ... which rounds up to .... workers.

(b) Complete this schedule for the workers, making sure that the project is completed in the minimum time. **(3)**

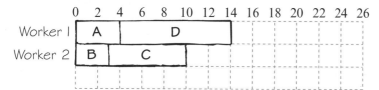

There is more than one possible solution.

2. This Gantt chart is for a manufacturing process that takes place over a period of 36 hours.

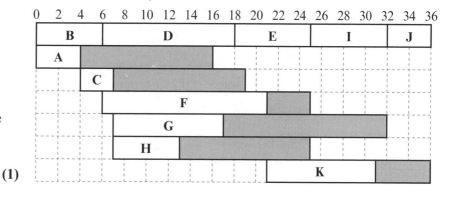

(a) Which activities are definitely taking place at time 12 hours? **(1)**

....

(b) Calculate a lower bound for the number of workers needed to finish the process in the minimum time. **(2)**

....

....

....

(c) Create a schedule for the workers on the grid below, making sure that the process is completed in the minimum time. **(4)**

Draw a scheduling diagram, not a Gantt chart.

Linear programming 1

Guided

1. A pet shop owner buys two brands of dry cat food for his shop. He pays £5 for a 2 kg bag of Happycat and £3 for a 2 kg bag of Moggie. He spends no more than £120 and buys at least 30 bags. He wants the number of bags of Happycat to be at least half of the number of bags of Moggie. The profit he makes on a bag of Happycat is £8 and on a bag of Moggie is £6. He wishes to maximise his profit, P.

> Define your variables before you start, making sure that they are both non-negative. State 'maximise' in your formulation.

> Don't try to solve the problem, you only need to formulate it.

Identify variables and formulate this information as a linear programming problem. **(6)**

Let x = number of bags of Happycat   Let y = number of bags of Moggie

$x \geqslant 0$ and $y \geqslant 0$ Cost = $5x + 3y$ so $5x + 3y \leqslant 120$

Total bags = $x + \text{............}$ so $\text{............} \geqslant 30$

....

2. A company manufactures tables and chairs. It takes 6 hours to make the parts for a table and 5 hours to make the parts for a chair. Assembly time for a table is 3 hours and for a chair is 1 hour. The time available for making the parts is 120 hours and for assembly is 36 hours. Tables are sold at a profit of £140 each and chairs at a profit of £80 each. The profit is to be maximised. This table shows a summary of this information.

Item of furniture	Production time (hours)	Assembly time (hours)	Profit (£)
Table	6	3	140
Chair	5	1	80
Time available	120	36	

Formulate this situation as a linear programming problem, defining your variables. **(5)**

....

....

....

3. A vet is treating a farm animal. She must provide at least a minimum daily dose of antibiotic, vitamin and nutrient. She can prescribe either tablets or liquid medicine. Tablets cost 90p each, and the liquid costs £2.40 per dose. The table shows what the tablets and the liquid medicine contain and also the daily dose needed.

	Antibiotic	Vitamin	Nutrient
Tablets (units per tablet)	2	4	5
Liquid (units per dose)	3	3	20
Daily dose needed	18	24	80

> This is a 'minimise' problem, so state this in your formulation.

The vet wants to treat the animal in the cheapest way.
Formulate this situation as a linear programming problem, defining your variables. **(6)**

....

....

....

....

Linear programming 2

Guided **1.** A linear programming problem is modelled by the following constraints.

$$5x + 4y \leqslant 200$$
$$2x + 5y \geqslant 100$$
$$y \geqslant 2x$$
$$x \geqslant 0 \text{ and } y \geqslant 0$$

Use the grid to represent these inequalities graphically.

Determine the feasible region and label it R.   **(5)**

> Label the lines clearly and take care with the shading – shade the **rejected** regions.

$5x + 4y = 200$: when $x = 0$, $y = 50$

and when $y = 0$, $x = 40$

$2x + 5y = 100$: when $x = 0$, $y = $ ....

and when $y = 0$, $x = $ ....

$y = 2x$: plot (0, 0) and (............ , ...)

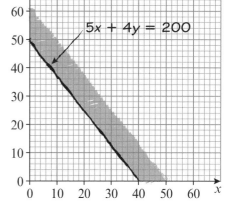

2. A linear programming problem is modelled by the following constraints.

$$2x + y \leqslant 80$$
$$5x + y \geqslant 100$$
$$3y \geqslant x$$
$$x \geqslant 0 \text{ and } y \geqslant 0$$

Use the grid to represent these inequalities graphically. Determine the feasible region and label it R.   **(5)**

....

....

....

....

3. This graph is being used to solve a linear programming problem. Two constraints are shown on the graph and the rejected regions are shaded.

(a) Write down the constraints shown on the graph.   **(4)**

....

....

Two further constraints are

$$3x + y \geqslant 60$$

and $$5x + 6y \leqslant 300$$

(b) Add two lines and shading to the graph to represent these constraints.
Determine the feasible region and label it R.   **(4)**

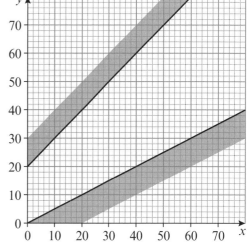

Objective lines

Guided 1. This diagram is being used to solve the following
linear programming problem.

Maximise **and** Minimise $P = 3x + 2y$

Subject to $4x + 5y \geqslant 100$

$15 \leqslant y \leqslant 30$

and $2x + y \leqslant 40$

The feasible region, R, is shown.

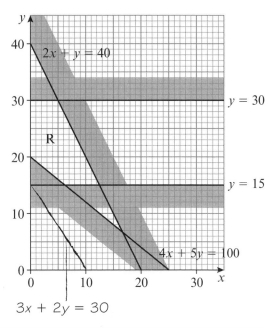

(a) Use the objective line method to find the two
optimal vertices and label them U and V.   **(3)**

$3x + 2y = 30$: (10, 0) and (0, 15)

lie on this line (the objective line).

> Choose a value to set $3x + 2y$ equal to in order
> to draw the objective line.

> Move your ruler parallel to the objective line and note where it enters and then leaves the feasible
> region. These are the vertices that maximise and minimise the objective function.

(b) Find the values of x and y that maximise and minimise the objective function $P = 3x + 2y$
and state the maximum and minimum values of P.   **(4)**

$U = ($ .... , ... $)$ $V = ($ .... , ... $)$

Minimum $P = $ ....   Maximum $P = $ ....

> U is for minimum P.
> V is for maximum P.

2. This diagram is being used to
solve the following linear
programming problem.

Maximise **and** Minimise

$P = x + 2y$

Subject to $2x + y \geqslant 80$

$2x + 5y \leqslant 200$

$x \leqslant 60$

and $y \geqslant 10$

The feasible region, R, is shown.

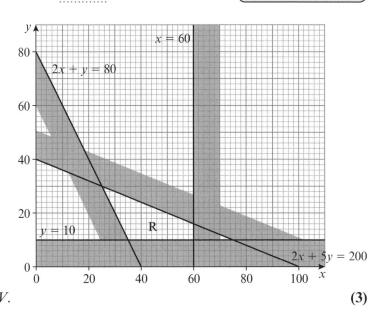

(a) Use the objective line method
to find the two optimal
vertices, and label them U and V.   **(3)**

....

(b) Find the values of x and y that maximise and minimise the objective function $P = x + 2y$
and state the maximum and minimum values of P.   **(4)**

....

....

....

Vertex testing

Guided

1. This graph is being used to solve a linear programming problem. These are the constraints.

$3x + y \geqslant 9$ $2x - y \leqslant 4$ $x \leqslant 4$

$y \leqslant 6$ $x \geqslant 0$ $y \geqslant 0$

Use the vertex testing method to minimise $P = 4x + 3y$ subject to these constraints, and write down the corresponding values of x and y. **(6)**

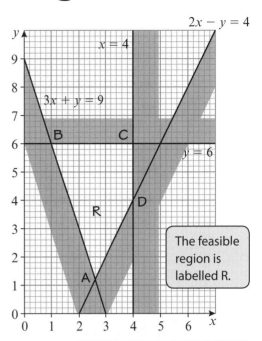

Solving simultaneously: $3x + y = 9$ ①

$2x - y = 4$ ②

① + ②: $5x = 13$, so $x = 2.6$

Substitute into ①: $3(2.6) + y = 9$,

so $y = 1.2$ (call this A)

From the graph, the other points of intersection are

$B = (1, \ldots\ldots)$, $C = (4, 6)$ and $D = (\ldots\ldots, \ldots\ldots)$

A: $x = 2.6$ $y = 1.2$ $P = 4x + 3y = \ldots\ldots\ldots$

B: $x = 1$ $y = \ldots\ldots$ $P = 4x + 3y = \ldots\ldots\ldots$

C: $x = 4$ $y = 6$ $P = 4x + 3y = 16 + 18 = 34$

D: $x = \ldots\ldots$ $y = \ldots\ldots$ $P = 4x + 3y = \ldots\ldots\ldots$

Minimum P is $\ldots\ldots$ when $x = \ldots\ldots$ and $y = \ldots\ldots$

> The feasible region is labelled R.

> Label the points of intersection clearly and solve equations simultaneously if you can't read the points of intersection from the graph.

> You must test all the vertices of the feasible region.

2. A linear programming problem has these constraints.

$5x + 3y \geqslant 30$ $4x - y \leqslant 7$ $y \leqslant 13$ $x \geqslant 1$ $y \geqslant 0$

(a) Use the grid to represent these inequalities graphically. Determine the feasible region and label it R. **(5)**

....

....

(b) Use the vertex testing method to minimise **and** maximise $P = 6y - 7x$ subject to these constraints.
Write down the corresponding values of x and y for the minimum and maximum values of P. **(5)**

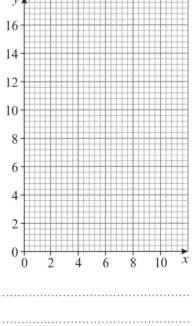

....

....

....

....

....

....

....

134

Matchings on graphs

Guided 1. The table shows which workers in a building firm can do which jobs.

	Masonry	Plumbing	Carpentry	Roofing	Electrics
Tom	✓				✓
Sam		✓			
Bill	✓		✓		
Gary		✓	✓		✓
Phil			✓	✓	

(a) Draw a bipartite graph to model this information. **(2)**

(b) Find the **two** possible complete matchings. **(4)**

> **S** must be matched with **P**, which means that **G** has to be matched with either **C** or **E**. This is your starting point for the two solutions.

2. Six people are playing a game. They must each choose a different coloured counter. They can pick from black, red, green, yellow, white and pink. This bipartite graph shows the original colour choices of six people.

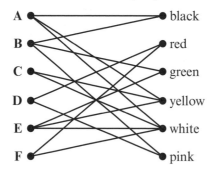

> **C** must be matched with white, which means that **A**, **E** and **F** cannot have white, they will have to have another colour. Use this as your starting point and try to match those people with the fewest alternatives first.

> There are two possible solutions.

Person **C** then decides that she doesn't want yellow; she will only play with the white counter. Find a complete matching, taking this into account. **(4)**

Maximum matchings

Guided

1. Figure 1 shows the possible allocations of six people to drinks they often choose. Figure 2 shows an initial matching for four of the friends.

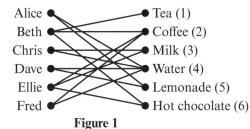 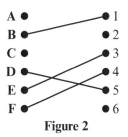 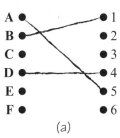

Alice Tea (1)
Beth Coffee (2)
Chris Milk (3)
Dave Water (4)
Ellie Lemonade (5)
Fred Hot chocolate (6)
Figure 1

A 1
B 2
C 3
D 4
E 5
F 6
Figure 2

A 1
B 2
C 3
D 4
E 5
F 6
(a)

(a) Starting from the initial matching in Figure 2, use the maximum matching algorithm to find an improved matching. State the alternating path and list and draw the improved matching. **(3)**

Alternating path: A − 5 = D − 4 = ... Change status: A = 5 − D = 4 − ....

New matching: A = 5, B = 1, ...

> An alternating path alternates between arcs that are in the initial matching and arcs that are not.

(b) Using your improved matching, find an alternating path to give a complete matching. State the alternating path and list and draw the complete matching. **(2)**

2. The bipartite graph shows a group of six friends and the European countries they would like to visit. An initial matching matches four of the friends.

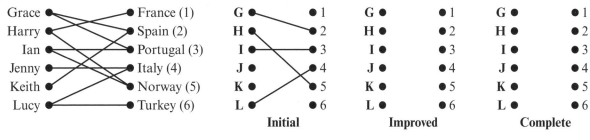

Grace France (1)
Harry Spain (2)
Ian Portugal (3)
Jenny Italy (4)
Keith Norway (5)
Lucy Turkey (6)

G 1
H 2
I 3
J 4
K 5
L 6
Initial

G 1
H 2
I 3
J 4
K 5
L 6
Improved

G 1
H 2
I 3
J 4
K 5
L 6
Complete

(a) Starting from this initial matching, use the maximum matching algorithm to find an improved matching. State the alternating path and list and draw the improved matching. **(3)**

....

....

(b) Using your improved matching, find an alternating path to give a complete matching. State the alternating path and list and draw the complete matching. **(2)**

....

....

Which algorithm?

1. Draw lines to match each problem to the most appropriate algorithm.   (3)

Putting a list into alphabetical or numerical
order, writing a full list after each pass.   ●   ●   Prim's algorithm

Finding a minimum spanning tree for a network,
listing the arcs included or rejected in the correct   ●   ●   First-fit decreasing
order.   bin-packing

Putting a list into alphabetical or numerical
order, showing all pivots.   ●   ●   Route inspection

Working out the shortest route to travel along all
arcs in a network.   ●   ●   Kruskal's algorithm

Finding a minimum spanning tree for a network
by selecting a vertex and adding the arc of least   ●   ●   Quick sort
weight that joins a new vertex to the tree.

Putting items listed in descending order into
equal-sized compartments, stating which items   ●   ●   Bubble sort
go in which compartment and in which order.

You are the examiner!

Checking through your work is a key skill for AS maths. Have a look at pages 138 and 139 of the *Revision Guide*, then practise with these questions. There are full worked solutions on page 182.

1. (a) Use a quick sort to put these English rivers into alphabetical order. You must make your pivots clear. **(5)**

     Ribble   Derwent   Calder   Lea   Tyne   Nene   Humber   Severn   Avon   Exe

....

....

....

....

....

....

> There are 10 elements, so the sixth element is the first pivot.

> You can mark the pivots. There will always be one element in the last line that is a new pivot, all the others will have been marked.

   (b) Use the binary search algorithm on your ordered list to locate the river Exe. **(4)**

....

....

....

....

> The first pivot is the sixth element.

> Write out a new list after each iteration. Don't stop when you reach one item – select it as a pivot and state that it has been found.

2. Here is a network.

   (a) Use Kruskal's algorithm to find a minimum spanning tree for this network. List the arcs in the order you consider them, stating whether or not they are to be included. **(2)**

....

....

   (b) Use Prim's algorithm, starting from **E**, to find a minimum spanning tree. Label the arcs in the order they are selected. **(2)**

....

....

   (c) Draw the minimum spanning tree and write down its weight. **(3)**

You are the examiner!

Checking through your work is a key skill for AS maths. Have a look at pages 138 and 139 of the *Revision Guide*, then practise with these questions. There are full worked solutions on page 182.

3. A company makes headphones and speakers. Each product uses two components, A and B. The table shows how much of each component is needed for each product and also how much of each component is available.

		Component A	Component B
Amount required per unit of product	**Headphones**	12	5
	Speakers	16	17
Amount available		672	425

There are certain constraints.

There must be more headphones than speakers.
There must be at least 5 sets of speakers.
The total output, of headphones and speakers combined, must be at least 20 units.

The profit on each unit of headphones is £30 and on each unit of speakers is £20.

The company wishes to maximise its profit.

> Be precise when you define your variables.

> There will be five inequalities, and an objective function. Remember to include the word 'maximise'.

(a) Formulate this situation as a linear programming problem, defining your variables.

(6)

....

....

....

(b) Use the grid below to represent these inequalities graphically. Determine the feasible region and label it R.

(5)

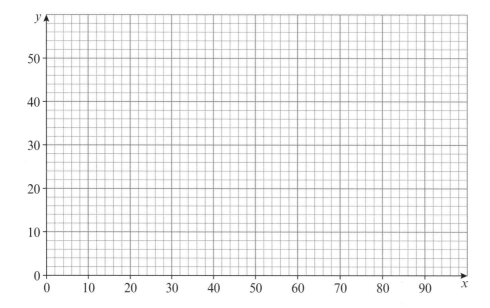

> Label the lines clearly and take care with the shading, making sure you shade the rejected region.

Calculators may NOT be used in this practice paper.

Time: 1 hour 30 minutes

Total marks: 75

You may use the Mathematical Formulae and Statistical Tables booklet which is available from the Edexcel website.

---

1. Express 16^{3x+2} in the form 2^y, stating y in terms of x.

(2)

---

2. Show that $\dfrac{4}{\sqrt{20} + \sqrt{12}}$ can be written in the form $\sqrt{a} - \sqrt{b}$, where a and b are integers.

(5)

---

3. Find $\displaystyle\int \left(2x^3 - 5 + \frac{3}{x^2}\right) dx$

giving each term in its simplest form.

(4)

---

4. The curve C has equation $y = 2x(x - 1)$ and the line L has equation $2y = 5x - 10$

Use algebra to show that C and L do not intersect.

(4)

---

5. Find the set of values for which

(a) $3x + 2 > 14 - x$

(2)

(b) $x(x + 6) > 16$

(4)

---

6. A curve with equation $y = f(x)$ is such that $f'(x) = 3x^2 - 14x + 8$

The curve passes through the point $(3, -1)$.

Find the equation of the curve.

(4)

---

7. A sequence of numbers $a_1, a_2, a_3, \ldots$ is defined by

$$a_1 = 5$$
$$a_{n+1} = 3a_n + c \qquad (n \geqslant 1)$$

where c is a constant.

(a) Write down an expression, in terms of c, for a_2.

(1)

(b) Show that $a_3 = 45 + 4c$

(2)

Given that $\displaystyle\sum_{i=1}^{4} a_i < 254$

(c) find the range of values of c.

(4)

140

8. A company offers two salary schemes for its employees.

   Scheme 1:   Salary in year 1 is £M.

               Salary increases by £$(2H)$ each year, forming an arithmetic sequence.

   Scheme 2:   Salary in year 1 is £$(M + 2100)$.

               Salary increases by £H each year, forming an arithmetic sequence.

   (a) Show that the **total** earned under Scheme 1 in 5 years is

       £$(5M + 20H)$

   (2)

   After 8 years the **total** earned is the same for both schemes.

   (b) Find the value of H.

   (4)

   For this value of H, an employee on Scheme 1 earns £30 800 in year 12

   (c) Find the value of M.

   (3)

---

9. The line L_1 has equation $5y + 2x + k = 0$, where k is a constant.

   Given that the point $A\,(-4, 2)$ lies on L_1, find

   (a) the value of k

   (1)

   (b) the gradient of L_1.

   (2)

   The line L_2 passes through A and is perpendicular to L_1.

   (c) Find the equation of L_2, giving your answer in the form $ax + by + c = 0$, where a, b and c are integers.

   (4)

   The line L_2 crosses the y-axis at the point B.

   (d) Find the coordinates of B.

   (2)

   (e) Find the exact length of AB.

   (2)

---

10. The curve C has equation $y = \frac{1}{4}x^3 - 4x^{\frac{3}{2}} - \frac{12}{x} + 18$, $x > 0$

    (a) Find $\dfrac{\mathrm{d}y}{\mathrm{d}x}$

    (4)

    (b) Show that the point $P\,(4, -1)$ lies on C.

    (2)

    (c) Find the equation of the normal to C at the point P, giving your answer in the form $ax + by + c = 0$, where a, b and c are integers.

    (5)

11. Figure 1 shows a sketch of the curve with equation

$$y = \frac{5}{x} \quad (x \neq 0)$$

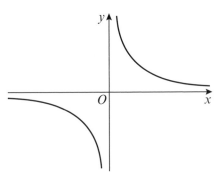

Figure 1

The curve C has equation $y = \frac{5}{x} - 4$ $(x \neq 0)$ and the line L has equation $y = 3x - 2$

(a) On a single diagram, sketch and clearly label the graphs of C and L.

On your diagram, show clearly the coordinates of the points where C and L cross the coordinate axes.

(5)

(b) Write down the equations of the asymptotes of the curve C.

(2)

(c) Find the coordinates of the points of intersection of $y = \frac{5}{x} - 4$ and $y = 3x - 2$

(5)

TOTAL FOR PAPER: 75 MARKS

Calculators may be used in this practice paper.
Time: 1 hour 30 minutes
Total marks: 75
You may use the Mathematical Formulae and Statistical Tables booklet which is available from the Edexcel website.

1.
$$y = \frac{6}{2x^2 - 3}$$

(a) Complete the table below, giving the values of y to 2 decimal places.

x	2	2.25	2.5	2.75	3
y	1.2			0.49	0.4

(2)

(b) Use the trapezium rule, with all the values of y from your table, to find an approximate value of

$$\int_2^3 \frac{6}{2x^2 - 3}\, dx$$

(4)

2. A geometric series has a second term of 270 and a fifth term of 80.

Giving your answers to 3 significant figures where appropriate, find

(a) the common ratio of the series

(2)

(b) the first term of the series

(2)

(c) the sum of the first 10 terms of the series

(2)

(d) the sum to infinity of the series.

(2)

3. $f(x) = x^4 + x^3 + ax^2 - 3x + b$

where a and b are constants.

When $f(x)$ is divided by $(x + 1)$ there is no remainder.

(a) Show that $a + b = -3$

(2)

When $f(x)$ is divided by $(x + 2)$, the remainder is -4.

(b) Find the value of a and the value of b.

(5)

4. (a) Find the first 4 terms of the binomial expansion, in ascending powers of x, of
$$\left(1 + \frac{x}{5}\right)^{10}$$
giving each term in its simplest form.

(4)

(b) Use your expansion to estimate the value of $(1.02)^{10}$, giving your answer to 4 decimal places.

(3)

5. (a) Given that

$$2\log_5(x - 4) - \log_5(2x - 13) = 1$$

show that $x^2 - 18x + 81 = 0$

(5)

(b) Hence, or otherwise, solve

$$2\log_5(x - 4) - \log_5(2x - 13) = 1$$

(2)

6. A curve has equation

$$y = x^3 - 7x^2 + 8x + 11$$

Use calculus to find the coordinates of the minimum point on this curve.

(8)

7. The circle C has equation

$$x^2 + y^2 - 24x + 12y + 80 = 0$$

The centre of the circle is at M.

(a) Find   (i) the coordinates of the point M

         (ii) the radius of the circle C.

(5)

N is the point with coordinates (22, 14).

(b) Find the length of the line MN, giving your answer in the form $a\sqrt{b}$, where a and b are integers.

(3)

The tangent to C at a point P on the circle passes through the point N.

(c) Find the length of the line NP.

(2)

8. (a) Solve, for $0 \leqslant x \leqslant 360°$, giving your answers in degrees to 1 decimal place

$$4\cos(x + 50°) = 3$$

(4)

(b) Find, for $0 \leqslant x \leqslant 2\pi$, all the solutions of

$$2\cos^2 x + 9\sin x + 3 = 0$$

giving your answers in radians.

You must show clearly how you obtained your answers.

(6)

9. Figure 1 shows the curve with equation $y = 2 - 4x - x^2$ and the line with equation $y = x + 6$

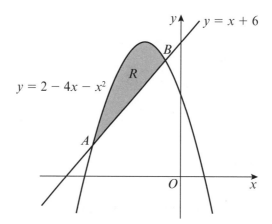

Figure 1

The curve and the line intersect at points A and B.

(a) Calculate the coordinates of the point A and the coordinates of the point B.

(5)

The shaded area R is bounded by the curve and the line, as shown in Figure 1.

(b) Calculate the exact area of R.

(7)

TOTAL FOR PAPER: 75 MARKS

Calculators may be used in this practice paper.
Time: 1 hour 30 minutes
Total marks: 75
You may use the Mathematical Formulae and Statistical Tables booklet which is available from the Edexcel website.

1. Two particles, A and B, have masses $6m$ and $2m$ respectively. The particles are moving towards each other on a smooth horizontal plane and collide directly. The speeds of A and B immediately before the collision are $3u$ and $4u$ respectively. Immediately after the collision, the speed of A is u and it continues in the same direction.

    (a) Find the speed and direction of motion of B immediately after the collision.

    (4)

    (b) Find the magnitude of the impulse exerted on A by B.

    (3)

2. A wooden beam ABC has length 12 m and mass 30 kg. The beam rests in equilibrium, in a horizontal position, on two smooth supports A and B, where $AB = 10$ m and A is at one end of the beam.

    A block of mass 40 kg is placed on the beam 3.2 m from A and a block of mass M kg is placed on the beam at the end C. The beam remains horizontal and in equilibrium. The forces exerted on the beam at supports A and B are equal.

    By modelling the beam as a uniform rod, and the blocks as particles

    (a) find the magnitude of the force exerted on the beam by the support at A

    (6)

    (b) find the value of M.

    (2)

3. A car is moving on a straight horizontal road. At time $t = 0$, the car is moving with speed 18 m s^{-1} and is at the point P. The car maintains the speed of 18 m s^{-1} for 30 s. It then moves with constant acceleration of 0.3 m s^{-2} until it reaches a speed of 24 m s^{-1}. The car then moves with constant speed 24 m s^{-1} for 40 s. It then moves with constant deceleration until it is moving with speed 10 m s^{-1} by the time it reaches point Q.

    (a) Sketch a speed–time graph to represent the motion of the car from P to Q.

    (3)

    (b) Find the time for which the car is accelerating.

    (2)

    Given that the distance from P to Q is 2855 m

    (c) find the time taken for the car to move from P to Q.

    (8)

4. A stone is projected vertically upwards from a point A with speed 18.6 m s^{-1}. After projection, the stone moves freely under gravity until it returns to A. The stone is modelled as a particle.

(a) Find the time for the stone to return to A.

(3)

(b) Find the greatest height above A reached by the stone.

(2)

(c) Find the length of time for which the stone is at least 9 m above A.

(6)

5. A particle of weight 90 N is placed on a fixed rough plane which is inclined at an angle α to the horizontal, where $\tan \alpha = \frac{4}{3}$. The coefficient of friction between the particle and the plane is $\frac{2}{3}$.

The particle is held at rest in equilibrium by a force of magnitude P newtons acting up the slope along the line of greatest slope of the plane through the particle, as shown in Figure 1.

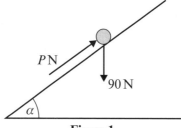

$P \text{ N}$

90 N

α

Figure 1

(a) Find the greatest possible value of P.

(8)

(b) Find the magnitude and direction of the frictional force acting on the particle when $P = 40$

(3)

6. [*In this question* **i** *and* **j** *are unit vectors due east and due north respectively. Position vectors are given relative to a fixed origin O.*]

Two cyclists P and Q are moving with constant velocities. Cyclist P moves with velocity $(6\mathbf{i} - 14\mathbf{j})\,\mathrm{km\,h}^{-1}$ and cyclist Q moves with velocity $(10\mathbf{i} - 12\mathbf{j})\,\mathrm{km\,h}^{-1}$.

At 10 am, cyclist P is at the point with position vector $(2\mathbf{i} + 5\mathbf{j})\,\mathrm{km}$ and cyclist Q is at the point with position vector $(-2\mathbf{i})\,\mathrm{km}$.

At time t hours after 10 am, the position vector of P is **p** km and the position vector of Q is **q** km.

(a) Write down expressions, in terms of t, for

    (i) **p**

    (ii) **q**

    (iii) $\overrightarrow{PQ}$.

(5)

(b) Find the time when P is due west of Q.

(2)

(c) Find the position vectors of P and Q when P is north-west of Q.

(4)

---

7. A particle P of mass 3 kg is moving up a fixed rough inclined plane at a constant speed of $13\,\mathrm{m\,s}^{-1}$ under the action of a force of magnitude 25 N. The plane is inclined at 40° to the horizontal. The force of 25 N acts in the vertical plane containing the line of greatest slope of the plane through P, and acts at 20° to the inclined plane, as shown in Figure 2. The coefficient of friction between P and the plane is μ.

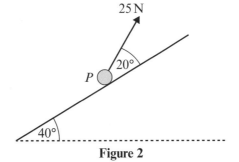

25 N

20°

P

40°

Figure 2

Find

(a) the magnitude of the normal reaction between P and the plane

(4)

(b) the value of μ.

(5)

The force of magnitude 25 N is removed.

(c) Find the distance that P travels between the instant when the force is removed and the instant when it comes to rest.

(5)

TOTAL FOR PAPER: 75 MARKS

S1
PRACTICE PAPER

Calculators may be used in this practice paper.
Time: 1 hour 30 minutes
Total marks: 75
You may use the Mathematical Formulae and Statistical Tables booklet which is available from the Edexcel website.

---

1. On a randomly chosen day, each of 80 students recorded the time, to the nearest minute, t minutes, they spent on a social networking site.

   The data are summarised in the following table.

   (a) Use linear interpolation to estimate the median time.

   (2)

   Given that $\sum ft = 4455$ and $\sum ft^2 = 319\,050$

   (b) estimate the mean and standard deviation of these times.

   Give your answers correct to 1 decimal place.

   (3)

Time, t (minutes)	Frequency
10–19	10
20–39	23
40–89	32
90–119	15

---

2. Over a period of time, a company gave an aptitude test to people applying for a job.

   The table shows a summary of the results.

   An outlier is an observation that falls either
   1.5 × interquartile range above the upper quartile or
   1.5 × interquartile range below the lower quartile.

   (a) On the graph paper below, draw a box plot to represent these data, indicating clearly any outliers.

   (5)

	Test score
Two lowest values	26, 36
Lower quartile	56
Median	68
Upper quartile	72
Two highest values	82, 88

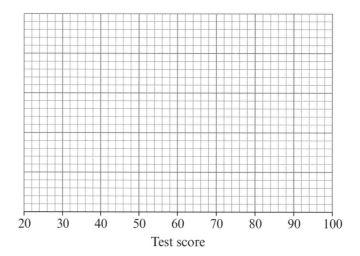

Test score

   (b) State the skewness of the distribution of test scores. Justify your answer.

   (2)

3. On a randomly chosen day, the probabilities that George travels to work by car, train or motorbike are $\frac{1}{8}$, $\frac{1}{2}$ and $\frac{3}{8}$ respectively.

The probabilities of him being on time when using these methods of travel are $\frac{2}{5}$, $\frac{4}{5}$ and $\frac{9}{10}$ respectively.

(a) Draw a tree diagram to represent this information.

(3)

(b) Find the probability that on a randomly chosen day George is late for work.

(3)

(c) Given that George is late for work, find the probability that he travelled by car.

(3)

4. The discrete random variable X can take only the values -1, 2, 3 or 4
For these values the cumulative distribution function is defined by

$$F(X) = \frac{x^2 + k}{25} \qquad x = -1, 2, 3, 4$$

(a) Show that $k = 9$

(2)

Find

(b) the probability distribution of X

(4)

(c) $E(X)$

(2)

(d) $E(X^2)$

(2)

(e) $Var(4 - 5X)$.

(3)

5. The fuel efficiency, y miles per gallon, and the weight carried, w kilograms, of each of 8 lorries were recorded.

The data for the weight carried was coded using $x = \frac{w - 5000}{200}$ and the following statistics were found.

$$\sum x = 69 \qquad \sum x^2 = 825 \qquad \sum y = 171 \qquad \sum y^2 = 3747 \qquad \sum xy = 1335 \qquad S_{yy} = 91.875$$

(a) Find S_{xx} and S_{xy} for these data.

(3)

(b) Calculate, to 3 significant figures, the product moment correlation coefficient between x and y.

(2)

(c) Find the equation of the regression line of y on x in the form $y = a + bx$

(6)

(d) Using this model, estimate the miles per gallon achieved by a lorry that carried a weight of 6500 kg.

(2)

6. Hens' eggs at a free-range farm have weights, X grams, that are normally distributed with mean 65 grams and standard deviation 5 grams.

The eggs are put into three categories.

    Medium   less than 62 grams $(X < 62)$

    Large   between 62 grams and 71 grams inclusive $(62 \leqslant X \leqslant 71)$

    Extra large   more than 71 grams $(X > 71)$

(a) Find the percentage of eggs in each category.

        (7)

(b) Two eggs are chosen at random.

Find the probability that they are both large eggs.

        (2)

The farm also has some ducks. The weights, Y grams, of duck eggs are normally distributed with mean μ grams and standard deviation σ grams.

(c) Given that $P(Y < 72.5) = 0.1$ and $P(Y > 81.3) = 0.2$, find the value of μ and the value of σ.

        (6)

7. Given that $P(A) = 0.4$, $P(B) = 0.48$ and $P(A \cup B) = 0.72$, find

(a) $P(A \cap B)$

        (2)

(b) $P(A' \cap B)$

        (1)

(c) $P(A' \mid B)$.

        (2)

The event C has $P(C) = 0.15$

The events B and C are mutually exclusive and the events A and C are independent.

(d) Find $P(A \cap C)$.

        (2)

(e) Draw a Venn diagram to illustrate the events A, B and C and the probability for each region.

        (4)

(f) Find $P(A \cup C')$.

        (2)

TOTAL FOR PAPER: 75 MARKS

Calculators may be used in this practice paper.
Time: 1 hour 30 minutes
Total marks: 75
Use the diagrams provided at the end of the paper on pages 156–157 to answer Questions 2, 4 and 8 (b) and (e).

1. Here are the lengths, in minutes, of some TV programmes.

   30   45   85   15   40   50   20

   Use a bubble sort to write this list in **descending** order. You only need to write down the final result of each pass.

   (4)

2. Figure 1 shows the possible allocation of six workers Alex (**A**), Ben (**B**), Chloe (**C**), Dan (**D**), Erin (**E**) and Frances (**F**) to six tasks 1, 2, 3, 4, 5 and 6.

   Figure 2 shows an initial matching.

   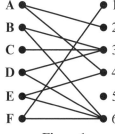

   Figure 1   **Figure 2**

   (a) Use the maximum matching algorithm once to find an improved matching using Diagram 1 on page 156.
   You must state the alternating path used and your improved matching.

   (3)

   (b) Explain why a complete matching is not possible.

   (2)

   After training, Ben adds task 2 to his possible allocations and Erin adds task 5 to her possible allocations.

   (c) **Starting with your improved matching**, use the maximum matching algorithm to obtain a complete matching using Diagram 1 on page 155. State the alternating path used and your final matching.

   (3)

3. The numbers in this list represent the weights, in kg, of fence posts that are to be transported in crates that will each hold a maximum weight of 30 kg.

   20   12   19   15   13   21   18

   (a) Calculate a lower bound for the number of crates that will be needed.

   (2)

   (b) Use the first-fit bin-packing algorithm to allocate the fence posts to the crates.

   (3)

   (c) Use the full-bins algorithm to allocate the fence posts to the crates.

   (2)

   (d) Explain why it is not possible to transport the fence posts using fewer crates than the number needed in part (c).

   (2)

4.

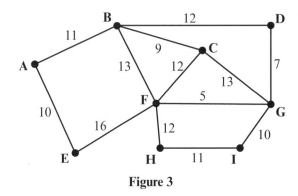

Figure 3

Figure 3 shows a network of roads between nine villages, **A**, **B**, **C**, **D**, **E**, **F**, **G**, **H** and **I**. The number on each arc represents the length, in miles, of the corresponding road.

(a) Use **Dijkstra's** algorithm to find the shortest distance from **A** to **I** using Diagram 2 on page 156. State the shortest route and its length.

(6)

(b) The road from **F** to **G** is closed for repairs to potholes. State the new shortest route and its length.

(2)

5. Figure 4 models a network of water pipes. The network shows a water source, **W**, used to supply water to fields at points **A**, **B**, **C**, **D**, **E** and **F**. The numbers on the arcs represent the lengths of the pipes, in metres, of the possible connections.

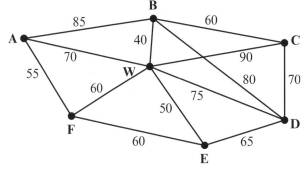

Figure 4

(a) Define the terms
   (i) tree
   (ii) minimum spanning tree.

(3)

(b) Use **Kruskal's** algorithm to find a minimum spanning tree for the network. You should list the arcs in the order in which you consider them. In each case, state whether the arc is to be included or rejected.

(3)

(c) Use **Prim's** algorithm, starting at **A**, to find a minimum spanning tree for the network. State clearly the order in which you include arcs in your tree.

(3)

(d) State whether your minimum spanning tree is unique. Justify your answer.

(1)

6. Figure 5 models a network of roads. The number on each arc represents the length, in km, of that road.

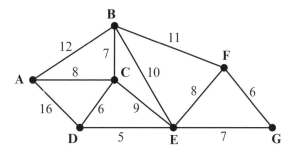

[The total weight of the network is 105 km]

Figure 5

The road markings are to be renewed, and to do this each road must be traversed at least once. The length of the route to be taken needs to be minimised.

(a) Use the route inspection algorithm, starting and finishing at **A**, to find a suitable route. State the length of the route and the arcs that have to be repeated. You must make your method and working clear.

(8)

A new road is to be built from **A** to **E**, of length 14 km.

(b) Determine if the addition of this new road will increase or decrease the length of the minimum route. You must make your reasoning clear.

(2)

7. Figure 6 shows a graph that is being used to solve a linear programming problem. Two of the constraints have been drawn on the graph and the rejected regions are shaded out.

(a) Write down, as inequalities, the constraints shown on the graph.

(4)

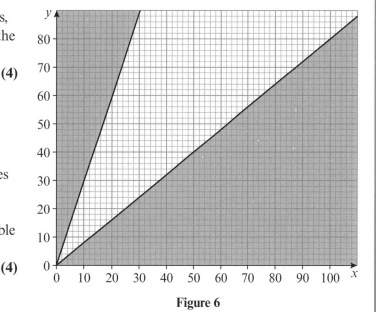

Two further constraints are
$$x + 4y \geqslant 80$$
$$4x + 5y \leqslant 400$$

(b) On the graph, add two lines and shading to represent these constraints.
Hence determine the feasible region and label it R.

(4)

Figure 6

The objective is to maximise
$$P = 4x + 3y$$

(c) Draw an objective line on the graph and use it to find the optimal solution. Label your objective line clearly.

(3)

8.

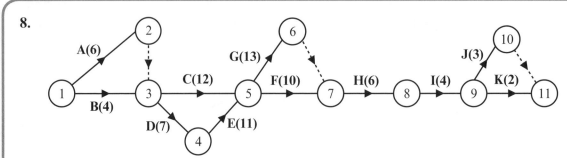

Figure 7

A project to build a bypass around a village is modelled by the network in Figure 7. The activities are represented by the arcs. The number in brackets on each arc gives the time, in weeks, to complete the activity. The project is to be completed in the shortest possible time.

(a) Explain why each of the following is necessary.

    (i) The dummy from event 2 to event 3

    (ii) The dummy from event 10 to event 11.

(3)

(b) On Diagram 3 on page 157, work out the early event times and the late event times.

(4)

(c) State the critical activities.

(2)

(d) Calculate the total float on activity **F**. You must make the numbers you use in your calculations clear.

(2)

(e) On Diagram 3 on page 157, draw a cascade (Gantt) chart for this project.

(4)

TOTAL FOR PAPER: 75 MARKS

Diagram 1 for Question 2

A ●   ● 1   A ●   ● 1

B ●   ● 2   B ●   ● 2

C ●   ● 3   C ●   ● 3

D ●   ● 4   D ●   ● 4

E ●   ● 5   E ●   ● 5

F ●   ● 6   F ●   ● 6

Diagram 2 for Question 4

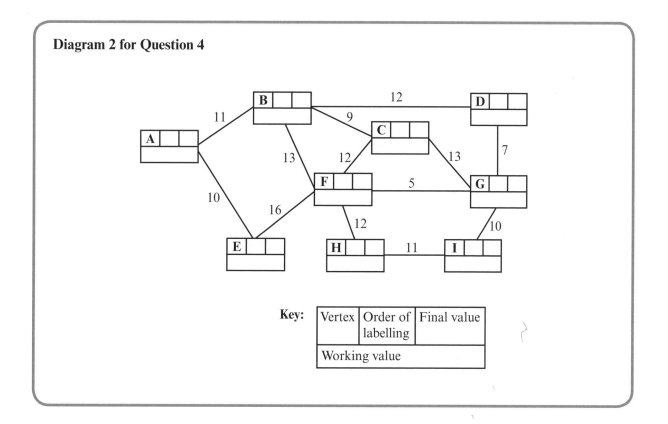

Key:

Vertex	Order of labelling	Final value
Working value		

Diagram 3 for Question 8

(b)

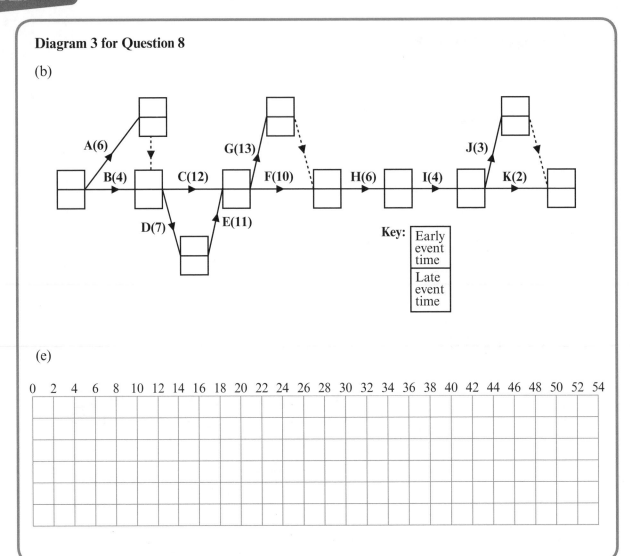

(e)

Answers

Worked solutions have been provided for all Guided questions. These are marked with a ⟩G⟩.
Short answers have been provided for all other questions.

Core Mathematics 1

1 Index laws

1. $\dfrac{1}{125}$

⟩G⟩ 2. $\sqrt{3}\left(27^{\frac{2}{3}}\right) = 3^{\frac{1}{2}} \times \left(27^{\frac{1}{3}}\right)^2 = 3^{\frac{1}{2}} \times 3^2 = 3^{\frac{5}{2}}$

3. $6x^{\frac{1}{4}}$

4. $5x^{\frac{2}{3}}$

⟩G⟩ 5. $\dfrac{\left(3x^{\frac{1}{2}}\right)^3}{9x^3} = \dfrac{27x^{\frac{3}{2}}}{9x^3} = 3x^{-\frac{3}{2}} = \dfrac{3}{x^{\frac{3}{2}}}$

6. $p = -\frac{1}{2}, q = 1$

7. $x = \frac{1}{2}$

8. $x = \frac{1}{2}$

2 Expanding and factorising

⟩G⟩ 1. $(x - 1)(x + 2)^2 = (x - 1)(x^2 + 4x + 4)$
   $= x^3 + 4x^2 + 4x - x^2 - 4x - 4 = x^3 + 3x^2 - 4$

⟩G⟩ 2. $x^3 - 9x = x(x^2 - 9) = x(x + 3)(x - 3)$

3. $x^3 - 3x^2 - 6x + 8$

4. $x(x + 5)(x - 1)$

5. $(2 - 3\sqrt{x})(2 - 3\sqrt{x}) = 4 - 6\sqrt{x} - 6\sqrt{x} + 9x$
   $= 4 - 12\sqrt{x} + 9x$
   $k = 12$

6. (a) $x(x^2 - x - 6)$ (b) $x(x - 3)(x + 2)$

3 Surds

1. $6\sqrt{2}$

⟩G⟩ 2. $\sqrt{18} + \sqrt{50} = \sqrt{9 \times 2} + \sqrt{25 \times 2} = 3 \times \sqrt{2} + 5 \times \sqrt{2} = 8\sqrt{2}$

⟩G⟩ 3. $\dfrac{\sqrt{5} + 3}{\sqrt{5} - 2} = \dfrac{(\sqrt{5} + 3)(\sqrt{5} + 2)}{(\sqrt{5} - 2)(\sqrt{5} + 2)} = \dfrac{5 + 5\sqrt{5} + 6}{5 - 4} = \dfrac{11 + 5\sqrt{5}}{1}$
   $= 11 + 5\sqrt{5}$

4. $12\sqrt{3}$

5. $23 - 3\sqrt{2}$

6. $52 - 14\sqrt{3}$

7. $12\sqrt{5} - 27$

4 Quadratic equations

1. $x = -2, x = \frac{4}{3}$

⟩G⟩ 2. (a) $x^2 - 10x + 15 = (x - 5)^2 - 25 + 15 = (x - 5)^2 - 10$
   (b) $(x - 5)^2 - 10 = 0$
   $(x - 5)^2 = 10$
   $(x - 5) = \pm\sqrt{10}$
   $x = 5 \pm \sqrt{10}$
   $c = 5, d = 1$

3. $p = -4, q = 10$

4. $a = 3, b = 1, c = 2$

5 The discriminant

⟩G⟩ 1. $a = 1, b = -2p, c = p$
   $b^2 - 4ac = (-2p)^2 - 4 \times 1 \times p = 4p^2 - 4p$
   $4p^2 - 4p = 0$
   $4p(p - 1) = 0$
   $p(p - 1) = 0$
   $p = 1$ (as $p \neq 0$)

⟩G⟩ 2. $3x^2 + kx - 5 - k = 0$
   $a = 3, b = k, c = -5 - k$
   $b^2 - 4ac = (k)^2 - 4 \times 3 \times (-5 - k) = k^2 + 12k + 60$
   For no real roots, $b^2 - 4ac < 0$ so $k^2 + 12k + 60 < 0$

3. -19

4. (a) $p^2 + 4p + 16$
   (b) $p^2 + 4p + 16 = (p + 2)^2 + 12$ giving $a = 2, b = 12$
   (c) $(p + 2)^2 \geqslant 0$ for all values of p,
      so $(p + 2)^2 + 12 > 0$,
      so there are real different roots for all values of p

6 Sketching quadratics

⟩G⟩ 1. When $x = 0$, $y = (0 - 3)(0 + 2) = -6$
   When $y = 0$, $0 = (x - 3)(x + 2)$
   so $x = 3$ or $x = -2$

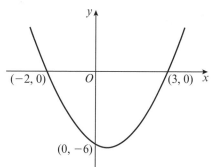

⟩G⟩ 2. (a) The coordinates of the vertex are $(-3, 4)$
      When $x = 0$, $y = (0 + 3)^2 + 4 = 13$

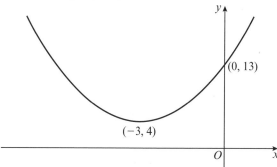

   (b) $(x + 3)^2 + 4 = x^2 + 6x + 13$
      $b^2 - 4ac = 36 - 52 = -16 < 0$ means no real roots,
      so the graph does not cross the x-axis

3.

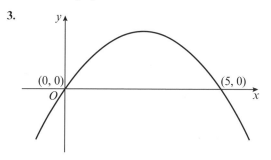

ANSWERS

7 Simultaneous equations

G 1. $y = x - 3$ ③
Substitute ③ into ②:
$x^2 - 2(x - 3) = 6$
$x^2 - 2x + 6 = 6$
$x^2 - 2x = 0$
$x(x - 2) = 0$
$x = 0, y = -3$ or $x = 2, y = -1$

2. $(-1, -4), (4, 1)$

3. (a) $x(x + 8) + 3x^2 = 16$ gives $4x^2 + 8x - 16 = 0$
so $x^2 + 2x - 4 = 0$
(b) $-1 \pm \sqrt{5}$

8 Inequalities

G 1. (a) $2x - 6 < 4 - 3x$
$5x < 10$ so $x < 2$
(b) $(2x - 5)(2 + x) = 0$
So $x = -2$ or $x = \frac{5}{2}$
For $y < 0$, $-2 < x < \frac{5}{2}$
(c) $-2 < x < 2$

2. $x \leqslant 3$ and $x \geqslant 5$

3. (a) $(2k)^2 - 4(3 - 2k) > 0$ gives $k^2 + 2k - 3 > 0$
(b) $k < -3$ and $k > 1$

9 Sketching cubics

G 1. When $y = 0$, $0 = x(x + 2)(x - 5)$
so $x = -2$ or $x = 0$ or $x = 5$

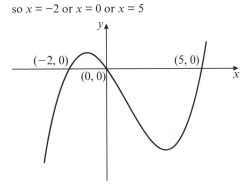

G 2. When $y = 0$, $0 = (x + 1)^2(3 - x)$ so $x = -1$ or $x = 3$
When $x = 0$, $y = (0 + 1)^2(3 - 0) = 3$

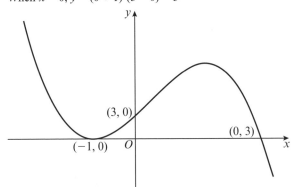

3.

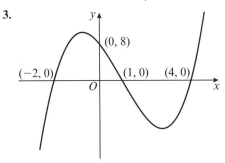

4. $x(3 + x)(3 - x)$

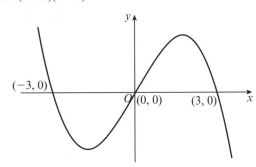

10 Transformations 1

G 1.

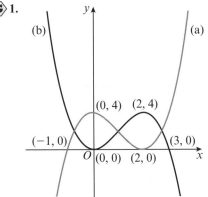

G 2. (a)

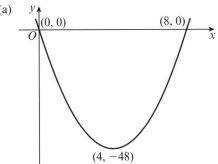

(b)

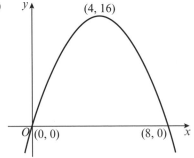

(c)

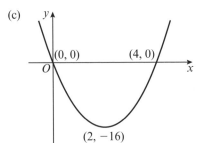

(d) $k = 4$

11 Transformations 2

 1. (a)

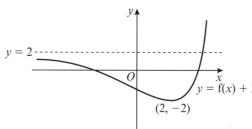

$y = 2$
$(2, -2)$
$y = f(x) + 3$

(b)

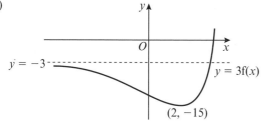

$y = -3$
$y = 3f(x)$
$(2, -15)$

(c)

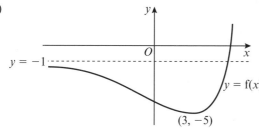

$y = -1$
$y = f(x)$
$(3, -5)$

 2. (a)

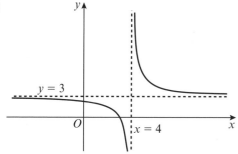

$y = 3$
$x = 4$

(b) $f(x - 3) = \dfrac{3(x - 3)}{(x - 3) - 1} = \dfrac{3(x - 3)}{x - 4}$

$(0, 2.25)$ and $(3, 0)$

12 Sketching $y = \dfrac{k}{x}$

 1. (a)

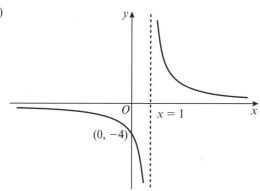

$x = 1$
$(0, -4)$

(b) $x = 1$ and $y = 0$

2. (a)

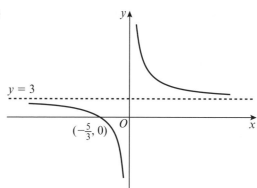

$y = 3$
$\left(-\frac{5}{3}, 0\right)$

(b) $x = 0$ and $y = 3$

13 Intersecting graphs

 1. (a)

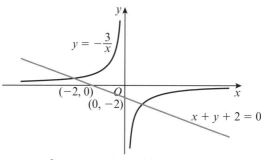

$y = -\dfrac{3}{x}$
$(-2, 0)$
$(0, -2)$
$x + y + 2 = 0$

(b) $y = -x - 2$
$-\dfrac{3}{x} = -x - 2$ so $-3 = -x^2 - 2x$
$x^2 + 2x - 3 = 0$
$(x + 3)(x - 1) = 0$
$(-3, 1)$ and $(1, -3)$

2. (a)

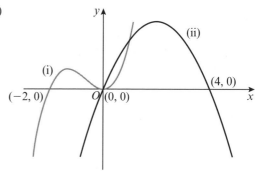

(ii)
(i)
$(-2, 0)$
O $(0, 0)$
$(4, 0)$

(b) $(0, 0)$ and $(1, 3)$ and $(-4, -32)$

14 Equations of lines

1. $y = 7 - 3 \times 3 = -2$

 2. $7y = 3 - 2x$
$y = \frac{3}{7} - \frac{2}{7}x$
Gradient $= -\frac{2}{7}$

 3. $x_1 = 3$, $y_1 = -2$, $m = -\frac{1}{3}$
$y - (-2) = -\frac{1}{3}(x - 3)$
$3(y + 2) = -1(x - 3)$
$3y + 6 = -x + 3$
$y = -\frac{1}{3}x - 1$

 4. (a) $x_1 = -2$, $y_1 = 1$, $x_2 = 6$, $y_2 = -2$
$m = \dfrac{y_2 - y_1}{x_2 - x_1} = \dfrac{-2 - 1}{6 + 2} = \dfrac{-3}{8}$

(b) $y - 1 = -\frac{3}{8}(x + 2)$
$8(y - 1) = -3(x + 2)$
$8y - 8 = -3x - 6$
$3x + 8y - 2 = 0$

5. (a) $p = 1$ (b) $4x + 3y - 17 = 0$

15 Parallel and perpendicular

⟩G⟩ 1. (a) $y = 4 - 3 \times 3 = -5$, so $(3, -5)$ lies on L

(b) Gradient of $L = -3$

Gradient of perpendicular line $= \frac{1}{3}$

Equation of perpendicular line through $(3, -5)$ is

$y + 5 = \frac{1}{3}(x - 3)$

$3y + 15 = x - 3$

$x - 3y - 18 = 0$

⟩G⟩ 2. (a) Coordinates of midpoint are $\left(\frac{-2 + 6}{2}, \frac{5 + 3}{2}\right) = (2, 4)$

(b) $4x - y - 4 = 0$

3. (a) $-\frac{3}{4}$

(b) $y = \frac{4}{3}x + \frac{5}{3}$

16 Lengths and areas

1. $p = 4$

⟩G⟩ 2. (a) $x + 3(x + 1) - 15 = 0$

$x + 3x + 3 - 15 = 0$

$4x = 12$

$x = 3$

Coordinates are $(3, 4)$.

(b) 32

3. 11.25

17 Arithmetic sequences

⟩G⟩ 1. (a) First term $n = 1 \qquad 3 \times 1 - 2 = 1$

Second term $n = 2 \qquad 3 \times 2 - 2 = 4$

Third term $n = 3 \qquad 3 \times 3 - 2 = 7$

(b) $d = 3$

⟩G⟩ 2. (a) $a = 40$, $d = -2.5$

20th term $= a + (20 - 1)d = 40 + 19 \times -2.5 = -7.5$

(b) $r = 17$

3. (a) $a + 14d = 9$ and $a + 19d = 16.5$

(b) $a = -12$, $d = 1.5$

4. $a = 40$, $d = 5$

18 Recurrence relations

⟩G⟩ 1. (a) $a_1 = 2$

$a_2 = 2a_1 - 3 = 4 - 3 = 1$

$a_3 = 2a_2 - 3 = 2 - 3 = -1$

(b) $a_4 = -5 \qquad a_5 = -13$

$a_1 + a_2 + a_3 + a_4 + a_5 = 2 + 1 - 1 - 5 - 13 = -16$

2. (a) $a_2 = 3k - 2$ (b) $a_3 = 3(3k - 2) - 2 = 9k - 8$

(c) $k = 2$

3. (a) $x_2 = p + 3$ (b) $x_3 = p(p + 3) + 3 = p^2 + 3p + 3$

(c) $p = -7$, $p = 4$

19 Arithmetic series

⟩G⟩ 1. $a = -8$, $d = 3$

$a + (n - 1)d = 19$

$-8 + (n - 1) \times 3 = 19$

$3n - 11 = 19$

$n = 10$

$S_{10} = \frac{1}{2} \times 10[2 \times -8 + (10 - 1) \times 3] = 55$

2. Sum $= 2500$

⟩G⟩ 3. (a) $S_{10} = \frac{10}{2}[2a + (10 - 1)d] = 150$

$5[2a + 9d] = 150$

$2a + 9d = 30$

(b) $a + 4d = 14$

(c) $a = 6$, $d = 2$

4. (a) $S_n = \frac{1}{2}n[2 \times 149 + (n - 1) \times -2] = 5000$

$n[149 + (n - 1) \times -1] = 5000$

$149n - n^2 + n = 5000$

$n^2 - 150n + 5000 = 0$

(b) $(n - 50)(n - 100) = 0$

$n = 50$ or $n = 100$

20 Sequence and series problems

⟩G⟩ 1. (a) $a = 600$, $d = 100$

25th year $= 600 + 24 \times 100 = £3000$

(b) $S_{25} = \frac{1}{2} \times 25[2 \times 600 + (25 - 1) \times 100]$

$= \frac{25}{2}[1200 + 2400]$

$= £45\,000$

⟩G⟩ 2. $a = 50$, $d = 10$

$S_w = \frac{1}{2}w(50 \times 2 + (w - 1) \times 10) = 12\,150$

$w(100 + 10w - 10) = 24\,300$

$10w(w + 9) = 24\,300$

$w(w + 9) = 2430 = 45 \times 54$

$w(w + 9) = 45 \times (45 + 9)$

$w = 45$

3. (a) $N = 36$

(b) $19\,700$

21 Differentiation 1

1. $5 - \frac{9}{2}x^{\frac{1}{2}} + 12x^2$

⟩G⟩ 2. $y = 5x^2 + 2x^{-1} - 3x^{-2}$

$\frac{dy}{dx} = 10x - 2x^{-2} + 6x^{-3}$

⟩G⟩ 3. $f(x) = \frac{3x - 2\sqrt{x}}{x} = \frac{3x}{x} - \frac{2\sqrt{x}}{x} = 3 - 2x^{-\frac{1}{2}}$

$f'(x) = x^{-\frac{3}{2}}$

4. (a) $5x^{-\frac{2}{3}} - 2x^{-1}$

(b) $\frac{dy}{dx} = 4 - \frac{10}{3}x^{-\frac{5}{3}} + 2x^{-2}$

5. $f'(x) = -16x^{-2} - 4x^{-\frac{3}{2}}$

22 Differentiation 2

1. (a) $\frac{dy}{dx} = 12x^2 - 3$

(b) $\frac{d^2y}{dx^2} = 24x$

⟩G⟩ 2. (a) When $x = 1$, $y = 5 \times 1 - \frac{2}{1^2} = 5 - 2 = 3$, so P lies on C

(b) $y = 5x - \frac{2}{x^2} = 5x - 2x^{-2}$

$\frac{dy}{dx} = 5 + 4x^{-3} = 5 + \frac{4}{x^3}$

When $x = 1$, $\frac{dy}{dx} = 5 + \frac{4}{1^3} = 9$

Gradient at $P = 9$

3. (a) $\frac{dy}{dx} = 6x^2 - 2x^{-\frac{1}{2}}$

(b) $24 - 1\sqrt{2}$

4. (a) $f'(x) = 3 + 4x^{-2}$

(b) $x = \pm\frac{2}{3}$

23 Tangents and normals

⟩G⟩ 1. $y = \frac{1}{3}x^3 + 2x^2 - 8x + 4$

$\frac{dy}{dx} = x^2 + 4x - 8$

When $x = 3$, $\frac{dy}{dx} = 3^2 + 4 \times 3 - 8 = 13$

Equation of tangent: $y - 7 = 13(x - 3)$ giving $y = 13x - 32$

G 2. (a) $y = 8 \times 4 + 2 \times 4^{\frac{3}{2}} - 3 \times 4^2 = 32 + 16 - 48 = 0$,
so $P(4, 0)$ lies on C

(b) $\dfrac{dy}{dx} = 8 + 3x^{\frac{1}{2}} - 6x$

(c) $\dfrac{dy}{dx} = 8 + 3x^{\frac{1}{2}} - 6x$

When $x = 4$, $\dfrac{dy}{dx} = 8 + 6 - 24 = -10$

Gradient of tangent $= -\dfrac{10}{1}$ so gradient of normal $= \dfrac{1}{10}$
Equation of normal: $y - 0 = \dfrac{1}{10}(x - 4)$
giving $x - 10y - 4 = 0$

3. (a) $y = x^3 + 2x^2 - 9x - 18$

$\dfrac{dy}{dx} = 3x^2 + 4x - 9$

(b) When $x = -3$, $\dfrac{dy}{dx} = 6$

$y - 0 = 6(x + 3)$
$y = 6x + 18$

(c) $3x^2 + 4x - 9 = 6$
$3x^2 + 4x - 15 = 0$
$(x + 3)(3x - 5) = 0$
$x = \dfrac{5}{3}$

24 Integration

G 1. $y = 4x - 3x^{-2}$

$\int y\,dx = \dfrac{4x^2}{2} - \dfrac{3x^{-1}}{-1} + c = 2x^2 + \dfrac{3}{x} + c$

G 2. $\int(3x^2 - 5 + x^{-\frac{1}{2}})\,dx = \dfrac{3x^3}{3} - 5x + 2x^{\frac{1}{2}} + c = x^3 - 5x + 2x^{\frac{1}{2}} + c$

3. $-3x^{-1} + \dfrac{3x^{-2}}{4} + c$

4. (a) $(3 - 2\sqrt{x})^2 = (3 - 2\sqrt{x})(3 - 2\sqrt{x}) = 9 - 12\sqrt{x} + 4x$, $k = 12$

(b) $9x - 8x^{\frac{3}{2}} + 2x^2 + c$

5. (a) $p = \dfrac{3}{2}$, $q = 2$

(b) $\dfrac{8x^{\frac{5}{2}}}{5} - \dfrac{2x^3}{3} + c$

25 Finding the constant

G 1. (a) $f(x) = \int\left(3x + \dfrac{2}{x^2}\right)dx$

$= \int(3x + 2x^{-2})\,dx$

$= \dfrac{3x^2}{2} - 2x^{-1} + c = \dfrac{3x^2}{2} - \dfrac{2}{x} + c$

$10 = \dfrac{3 \times 4}{2} - \dfrac{2}{2} + c$

$c = 5$

$f(x) = \dfrac{3x^2}{2} - \dfrac{2}{x} + 5$

(b) $f(x) = \dfrac{3x^2}{2} - \dfrac{2}{x} + 5$

$f(-1) = \dfrac{3}{2} + 2 + 5 = 8.5$

G 2. $\dfrac{dy}{dx} = \dfrac{x - 3}{\sqrt{x}} = x^{\frac{1}{2}} - 3x^{-\frac{1}{2}}$

$y = \int(x^{\frac{1}{2}} - 3x^{-\frac{1}{2}})\,dx = \dfrac{2x^{\frac{3}{2}}}{3} - 6x^{\frac{1}{2}} + c$

$\dfrac{1}{3} = \dfrac{2 \times 8}{3} - 6 \times 2 + c$

$c = 7$

$y = \dfrac{2x^{\frac{3}{2}}}{3} - 6x^{\frac{1}{2}} + 7$

3. (a) $\dfrac{dy}{dx} = \dfrac{(x^2 - 2)^2}{x^2} = \dfrac{(x^2 - 2)(x^2 - 2)}{x^2} = \dfrac{x^4 - 4x^2 + 4}{x^2}$

$\dfrac{dy}{dx} = x^2 - 4 + 4x^{-2}$

(b) $y = \dfrac{x^3}{3} - 4x - 4x^{-1} + 5$

26–27 You are the examiner!

1. $\dfrac{(4 + 2\sqrt{5})}{(3 + \sqrt{5})} = \dfrac{(4 + 2\sqrt{5})(3 - \sqrt{5})}{(3 + \sqrt{5})(3 - \sqrt{5})}$

$= \dfrac{12 - 4\sqrt{5} + 6\sqrt{5} - 2 \times 5}{3^2 - 5}$

$= \dfrac{2 + 2\sqrt{5}}{4}$

$= \dfrac{1}{2} + \dfrac{1}{2}\sqrt{5}$

2. $a = 1$, $b = -4p$, $c = 2p$
For equal roots, $b^2 - 4ac = 0$
$(-4p)^2 - 8p = 0$
$16p^2 - 8p = 0$
$8p(2p - 1) = 0$
$p = 0$ or $p = \dfrac{1}{2}$
But p is a non-zero constant, so $p = \dfrac{1}{2}$

3. $\int(6x^2 - 4x^{-2} + 3x^{\frac{1}{2}})\,dx = \dfrac{6x^3}{3} - \dfrac{4x^{-1}}{-1} + \dfrac{3x^{\frac{3}{2}}}{\frac{3}{2}} + c$

$= 2x^3 + \dfrac{4}{x} + 2x^{\frac{3}{2}} + c$

4. (a) $3x - 15 > 6 - 4x$
$7x > 21$
$x > 3$

(b) $x^2 - 3x - 10 > 0$
$(x - 5)(x + 2) > 0$

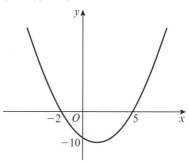

$x < -2$ or $x > 5$

(c)

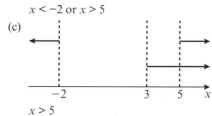

$x > 5$

5. (a) When $x = 0$, $y = (-2)^2 = 4$
When $y = 0$, $x = 2$ (repeated root)

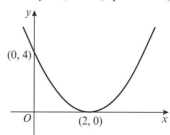

(b) When $x = 0$, $y = (-2)^2 + k = 4 + k$
The coordinates of the vertex are $(2, k)$.

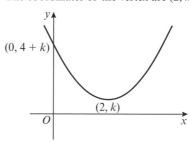

Core Mathematics 2

28 The factor theorem

G> 1. (a) $f(x) = 2x^3 - 3x^2 - 11x + 6$

$f(-2) = 2(-2)^3 - 3(-2)^2 - 11(-2) + 6$

$= -16 - 12 + 22 + 6$

$= 0$

So $(x + 2)$ is a factor.

(b)
$$
\begin{array}{r|rrrr}
-2 & 2 & -3 & -11 & 6 \\
 & \downarrow & -4 & 14 & -6 \\
\hline
 & 2 & -7 & 3 & 0
\end{array}
$$

$f(x) = (x + 2)(2x^2 - 7x + 3)$

$= (x + 2)(2x - 1)(x - 3)$

2. (a) $c = -24$ (b) $(x - 4)(2x + 3)(x + 2)$

3. $x = -5, x = -\frac{1}{2}, x = -4$

29 Remainder theorem

G> 1. (i) $f(x) = 2x^3 + 3x^2 - 7x - 2$

$f(-3) = 2(-3)^3 + 3(-3)^2 - 7(-3) - 2$

$= -54 + 27 + 21 - 2 = -8$

(ii) $f(\frac{1}{2}) = 2(\frac{1}{2})^3 + 3(\frac{1}{2})^2 - 7(\frac{1}{2}) - 2 = \frac{1}{4} + \frac{3}{4} - 3.5 - 2 = -4.5$

G> 2. (a) $f(2) = 2(2)^3 + a(2)^2 + b(2) + 3 = 27$

$16 + 4a + 2b + 3 = 27$

$4a + 2b = 8$

$2a + b = 4$

(b) $f(-1) = 2(-1)^3 + a(-1)^2 + b(-1) + 3 = 12$

$-2 + a - b + 3 = 12$

$a - b = 11$

$a = 5, b = -6$

3. $a = 3, b = 7$

30 Equation of a circle

1. $(x - 4)^2 + (y + 1)^2 = 6^2$

G> 2. (a) $r = \sqrt{(-1 - 2)^2 + (7 - 3)^2} = 5$

$(x - 2)^2 + (y - 3)^2 = r^2$

$(x - 2)^2 + (y - 3)^2 = 25$

(b) $(5 - 2)^2 + (7 - 3)^2 = 3^2 + 4^2 = 9 + 16 = 25$

so $(5, 7)$ lies on C.

G> 3. (a) $x^2 + 2x + y^2 - 6y = 6$

$(x + 1)^2 - 1 + (y - 3)^2 - 9 = 6$

$(x + 1)^2 + (y - 3)^2 = 16$

Centre $(-1, 3)$; radius 4

(b) $y = 0$: $(x + 1)^2 + (0 - 3)^2 = 16$

$(x + 1)^2 + 9 = 16$

$(x + 1)^2 = 7$

$x = -1 \pm \sqrt{7}$ so coordinates are $(-1 + \sqrt{7}, 0)$ and $(-1 - \sqrt{7}, 0)$

4. $(x - 1)^2 + (y - 8)^2 = 25$

31 Circle properties

1. Equation is $(x + 2)^2 + (y - 3)^2 = 25$; centre $(-2, 3)$, radius 5

Midpoint of PQ is $(-2, 3)$ so PQ is diameter.

G> 2. (a) Gradient of tangent $= \frac{3}{5}$

Gradient of line through P and $Q = -\frac{5}{3}$

Equation of line is $y - y_1 = m(x - x_1)$

$y - 7 = -\frac{5}{3}(x - 1)$

$3y - 21 = -5x + 5$

$5x + 3y - 26 = 0$

(b) $Q (4, 2)$

3. $a = 9$

32 Geometric sequences

1. 15th term $= 0.888$ (3 s.f.)

G> 2. (a) Fourth term: $ar^3 = 72$ ①

Seventh term: $ar^6 = 9$ ②

② ÷ ①: $\frac{ar^6}{ar^3} = r^3 = \frac{9}{72} = \frac{1}{8}$

$r = \frac{1}{2}$

(b) $ar^3 = 72$ so $a = 576$

G> 3. $\frac{15}{k} = \frac{k + 40}{15}$

$225 = k^2 + 40k$

$k^2 + 40k - 225 = 0$

$(k + 45)(k - 5) = 0$

$k = 5, k = -45$

4. (a) $\frac{k}{k + 6} = \frac{2k - 16}{k}$

$k^2 = (k + 6)(2k - 16)$ gives $k^2 - 4k - 96 = 0$

(b) $(k - 12)(k + 8) = 0$ so $k = 12$ (or $k = -8$ which is not possible as k is positive)

(c) $r = \frac{2}{3}$

33 Geometric series

G> 1. $S_{20} = \frac{150(1 - \frac{2}{3}^{20})}{1 - \frac{2}{3}} = 449.9$ (1 d.p.)

G> 2. $\sum_{k=1}^{8} 10(3^k) = 30 + 90 + 270 + 810 + \ldots$

$a = 30, \quad r = 3$

$S_8 = \frac{30(1 - 3^8)}{1 - 3} = 98\,400$

3. $S_{50} = -33\,088.9$

4. $S_n = \frac{3^n - 1}{2}$

5. (a) £41 500

(b) £593 000

34 Infinite series

G> 1. $a = \frac{2}{3}$ $r = \frac{1}{2} \div \frac{2}{3} = \frac{3}{4}$

$S_\infty = \frac{a}{1 - r} = \frac{\frac{2}{3}}{1 - \frac{3}{4}} = \frac{8}{3}$

G> 2. $a = 150$ $S_\infty = \frac{a}{1 - r} = \frac{150}{1 - r} = 375$

$150 = 375(1 - r)$ so $r = \frac{3}{5}$

3. (a) $S_\infty = 150$

(b) $-1 < r < 1$

(c) 0.773

4. (a) $ar = 12$, so $a = \frac{12}{r}$

$\frac{12}{r(1 - r)} = 50$ gives $25r^2 - 25r + 6 = 0$

(b) $r = \frac{3}{5}$ and $a = 20$, or $r = \frac{2}{5}$ and $a = 30$

35 Binomial expansion

G> 1. $a = 3$ $b = -2x$ $n = 5$

$(3 - 2x)^5 = (3)^5 + \binom{5}{1}(3)^4(-2x) + \binom{5}{2}(3)^3(-2x)^2 + \ldots$

$= 243 + [5 \times 81 \times (-2x)] + [10 \times 27 \times 4x^2] + \ldots$

$\approx 243 - 810x + 1080x^2$

G> 2. (a) $a = 1$ $b = px$ $n = 9$

$(1 + px)^9 = 1^9 + \binom{9}{1}1^8px + \binom{9}{2}1^7(px)^2 + \ldots$

$\approx 1 + 9px + 36p^2x^2$

(b) $(1 + px)^9 = 1 + 9px + 36p^2x^2 + \ldots$

$9p = q \qquad 36p^2 = 20q$

$36p^2 = 20 \times 9p$

$p^2 = 5p$

$p = 5, q = 45$

3. $16\,384 - 86\,016x + 193\,536x^2$

4. (a) $64 + 192kx + 240k^2x^2$

(b) $k = 5, q = 240$

36 Solving binomial problems

1. $n = 12 \qquad r = 7 \qquad a = 4 \qquad b = -\frac{x}{2}$

$\binom{12}{7}4^5\left(-\frac{x}{2}\right)^7 = 792 \times 1024 \times -\frac{x^7}{128} = -6336x^7$

Coefficient $= -6336$

2. $1 + \frac{x}{2} = 1.005$

$x = 0.01$

$(1.005)^8 \approx 1 + 4(0.01) + 7(0.01)^2 + 7(0.01)^3$

$\approx 1.040\,71$ (5 d.p.)

3. (a) $\left(1 + \frac{x}{4}\right)^9 \approx 1 + \frac{9x}{4} + \frac{9x^2}{4} + \frac{21x^3}{16}$

(b) 1.2488

4. (a) $(1 - 2x)^7 = 1 - 14x + 84x^2 - 280x^3$

(b) $(1 + x)(1 - 14x) \approx 1 - 14x + x = 1 - 13x$

37 Radians, arcs and sectors

1. (a) $9 = 6\theta, \theta = \frac{9}{6} = 1.5\,\text{rad}$

(b) Area $= \frac{1}{2}r^2\theta = \frac{1}{2} \times 6^2 \times 1.5 = 27\,\text{cm}^2$

2. (a) Arc length $= r\theta = 10 \times 0.65 = 6.5\,\text{cm}$

Perimeter $= 6.5 + 10 + 10 = 26.5\,\text{cm}$

(b) Area $= \frac{1}{2}r^2\theta = \frac{1}{2} \times 10^2 \times 0.65 = 32.5\,\text{cm}^2$

3. (a) Arc length $PR = \frac{14\pi}{3}\,\text{cm}$

(b) Area of sector $= \frac{49\pi}{3}\,\text{cm}^2$

4. (a) $1.41\,\text{rad}$

(b) $27.3\,\text{cm}$

38 The cosine rule

1. $a^2 = b^2 + c^2 - 2bc\cos A$

$a^2 = 5^2 + 8^2 - 2 \times 5 \times 8\cos 2.1 = 129.387$

$a = 11.4\,\text{cm}$ (3 s.f.)

2. $\cos B = \frac{a^2 + c^2 - b^2}{2ac}$

$= \frac{9^2 + 6^2 - 12^2}{2 \times 6 \times 9} = -\frac{1}{4}$

$B = \cos^{-1}(-0.25) = 1.82\,\text{rad}$

3. (a) $\cos A = \frac{8^2 + 4^2 - 6^2}{2 \times 8 \times 4} = \frac{44}{64} = \frac{11}{16}$

(b) $\sin A = \frac{3\sqrt{15}}{16}$

4. $437\,\text{m}$

39 Sine rule

1. $\angle ABC = \pi - 0.9 - 1.1 = 1.142$

$\frac{b}{\sin B} = \frac{c}{\sin C}$

$\frac{9}{\sin 1.142} = \frac{c}{\sin 1.1}$

so $c = \frac{9\sin 1.1}{\sin 1.142} = 8.82\,\text{cm}$ (3 s.f.)

2. (a) $\frac{\sin x}{14} = \frac{\sin 0.3}{8}$

$\sin x = \frac{14\sin 0.3}{8} = 0.517$ (3 d.p.)

(b) $x = \sin^{-1}(0.517) = 0.54$

or $x = \pi - (0.54) = 2.60$ (2 d.p.)

3. $BC = 29.0\,\text{cm}$

4. $\angle ACB = 36°$

40 Areas of triangles

1. (a) $\cos Q = \frac{PQ^2 + QR^2 - PR^2}{2 \times PQ \times QR}$

$= \frac{(5\sqrt{2})^2 + (5\sqrt{2})^2 - (10)^2}{2 \times 5\sqrt{2} \times 5\sqrt{2}} = \frac{100 - 100}{100} = 0$

$Q = \frac{\pi}{2}$

(b) Area of sector $= \frac{1}{2}r^2\theta = \frac{1}{2} \times (5\sqrt{2})^2 \times \frac{\pi}{2} = \frac{50\pi}{4}$

Area $= \frac{25\pi}{2}\,\text{cm}^2$

(c) Area of triangle $= \frac{1}{2}ab\sin\theta$

$= \frac{1}{2} \times 5\sqrt{2} \times 5\sqrt{2} \times \sin\frac{\pi}{2}$

$= 25$

Area $= 25\,\text{cm}^2$

2. Area of $ABC = \frac{1}{2} \times 9 \times 12 \times \sin 0.8 = 38.737\ldots$

Area of $ABD = \frac{1}{2} \times 9^2 \times 0.8 = 32.4\,\text{cm}^2$

Area of $R = 38.737 - 32.4 = 6.34\,\text{cm}^2$

3. Area of $R = 10.8\,\text{cm}^2$

41 Trigonometric graphs

1. (a)

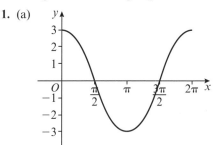

(b) $(0, 3), (\pi, -3), (2\pi, 3)$

2. (a)

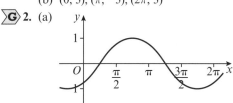

(b) When $x = 0$: $y = \sin\left(0 - \frac{\pi}{3}\right) = -\sin\left(\frac{\pi}{3}\right) = -\frac{\sqrt{3}}{2}$

$\left(0, -\frac{\sqrt{3}}{2}\right)$

When $y = 0$: $0 = \sin\left(x - \frac{\pi}{3}\right)$,

so $x = 0 + \frac{\pi}{3} = \frac{\pi}{3}$

or $x = \pi + \frac{\pi}{3} = \frac{4\pi}{3}$

$\left(\frac{\pi}{3}, 0\right), \left(\frac{4\pi}{3}, 0\right)$

3. $a = 2, b = \frac{\pi}{4}$

42 Trigonometric equations 1

1. $\sin x = \frac{2}{5} = 0.4$

$x = \sin^{-1}(0.4) = 0.412$ or $x = \pi - 0.412 = 2.730$

2. $\tan x = 3$

$x = \tan^{-1}(3) = 71.6°$

or $x = 180° + 71.6° = 251.6°$

3. (a)

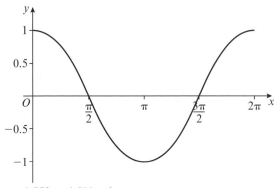

(b) $x = 1.772$ or 4.511 rad

4. (a) $x = -36.9°$ or $-143.1°$ (b) $x = -48.2°$ or $48.2°$

43 Trigonometric identities

G 1. (a) $3\sin x = 2\cos^2 x$

$\sin^2 x + \cos^2 x = 1$ so $\cos^2 x = 1 - \sin^2 x$

$3\sin x = 2(1 - \sin^2 x)$

so $2\sin^2 x + 3\sin x - 2 = 0$

(b) $2\sin^2 x + 3\sin x - 2 = 0$

$(2\sin x - 1)(\sin x + 2) = 0$

$\sin x = \frac{1}{2}$ $(\sin x \ne -2)$

$x = 30°$ or $x = 150°$

G 2. (a) $\dfrac{\sin\theta}{\cos\theta} = \dfrac{2}{3}$

$\tan\theta = \dfrac{2}{3}$

(b) $\theta = \tan^{-1}\left(\dfrac{2}{3}\right)$

$\theta = 33.7°$ or $\theta = 213.7°$

3. $\theta = \dfrac{\pi}{4}$ or $\dfrac{5\pi}{4}$ or $\dfrac{7\pi}{6}$ or $\dfrac{11\pi}{6}$

4. (a) $\cos\theta\tan\theta = 4\cos^2\theta + 1$

$\cos\theta\dfrac{\sin\theta}{\cos\theta} = 4\cos^2\theta + 1$

$\sin\theta = 4(1 - \sin^2\theta) + 1$

$4\sin^2\theta + \sin\theta - 5 = 0$

(b) $\theta = 90°$

44 Trigonometric equations 2

G 1. (a) $0 \le 2x \le 360°$. Let $Z = 2x$

$Z = \sin^{-1}\left(\frac{1}{2}\right) = 30°$

or $Z = 180 - 30 = 150°$

$2x = 30°$ or $150°$

$x = 15°$ or $x = 75°$

(b) $-50° \le x - 50° \le 130°$. Let $Z = X - 50°$

$Z = \cos^{-1}(0.3) = 72.5°$

or $Z = 360 - 72.5 = 287.5°$ (outside range)

$x - 50° = 72.5°$

$x = 122.5°$

2. $-2.737, 0.405$ rad

3. (a) $\theta = 38.6°, 121.4°$

(b) $\theta = 60°, 120°, 240°, 300°$

45 Logarithms

G 1. (a) $8^2 = 64$ so $\log_8 64 = 2$

(b) $3\log_a 2 = \log_a 2^3 = \log_a 8$

$\log_a 8 + \log_a 7 = \log_a(8 \times 7) = \log_a 56$

2. (a) $p = \frac{1}{16}$ (b) $y = 5$ (c) $\frac{4}{3}$

3. (a) $\log_a 200$ (b) $\log_a \frac{27}{4}$

G 4. $\log_4 y = \log_4 4x^3$

$\log_4 y = \log_4 4 + \log_4 x^3$

$\log_4 y = 1 + 3\log_4 x$

5. $y^2 = 9x^4$

$\log_3 y^2 = \log_3 9x^4$

$2\log_3 y = \log_3 9 + \log_3 x^4$

$2\log_3 y = \log_3 3^2 + 4\log_3 x$

$2\log_3 y = 2\log_3 3 + 4\log_3 x$

$2\log_3 y = 2 + 4\log_3 x$

$\log_3 y = 1 + 2\log_3 x$

46 Equations with logs

G 1. $\log_3 \dfrac{2x - 1}{x} = 1$

$\dfrac{2x - 1}{x} = 3^1$

$2x - 1 = 3x$

$x = -1$

2. $x = \frac{1}{2}$

G 3. $a = 4b$ ①

$\log_2 a + \log_2 b = 3$ ②

$\log_2 4b + \log_2 b = 3$

$\log_2 4b^2 = 3$

$4b^2 = 2^3$

$4b^2 = 8$

$b^2 = 2$

$b = \sqrt{2}$ and $a = 4\sqrt{2}$ (a and b both positive)

4. (a) $2\log_2(x - 2) - \log_2(6 - x) = 1$

$\log_2 \dfrac{(x - 2)^2}{(6 - x)} = 1$

$\dfrac{(x - 2)^2}{(6 - x)} = 2^1$

$x^2 - 4x + 4 = 2(6 - x)$

$x^2 - 2x - 8 = 0$

(b) $x = 4$ $(x \ne -2)$

5. $x = 27$ or $\frac{1}{27}$

47 Exponential equations

G 1. (a) $3^x = 5$

$\log 3^x = \log 5$

$x\log 3 = \log 5$

$x = \dfrac{\log 5}{\log 3} = 1.46$

(b) Let $Y = 3^x$ so $3^{2x} = (3^x)^2 = Y^2$

$Y^2 - 8Y + 15 = 0$

$(Y - 3)(Y - 5) = 0$

$Y = 3$ or 5, so $3^x = 3$ or 5

$x = 1$ or $x = \dfrac{\log 5}{\log 3} = 1.46$

2. (a)

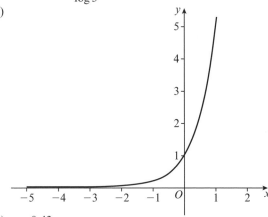

(b) $x = 0.43$

3.

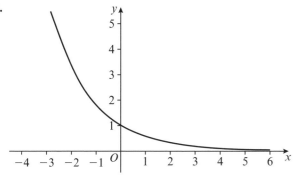

4. $x = 0$, $x = 0.936$

48 Series and logs

G 1. $a = 12$ $r = 2.5$ $S_n = \dfrac{a(1 - r^n)}{1 - r}$

$\dfrac{12(1 - 2.5^n)}{1 - 2.5} > 20\,000$

$12(1 - 2.5^n) < -30\,000$

$1 - 2.5^n < -2500$

$2501 < 2.5^n$

$2.5^n > 2501$

$n \log 2.5 > \log 2501$

$n > 8.539$

$n = 9$

2. $a = 25\,000$ $r = 0.85$ nth term $= ar^{n-1}$

$25\,000 \times 0.85^{n-1} < 1500$

$0.85^{n-1} < 0.06$

$(n - 1) > \dfrac{\log 0.06}{\log 0.85}$

$n - 1 > 17.31$

$n > 18.31$

$n = 19$

so $m = 19 - 1 = 18$

($m = n - 1$ because first term is $a = 25\,000$)

3. $n = 5$

4. (a) $a = 250\,000$ $r = 1.04$

$250\,000 \times 1.04^{N-1} > 500\,000$

$1.04^{N-1} > 2$

$(N - 1) \log 1.04 > \log 2$

(b) $N = 19$

49 Stationary points 1

G 1. $\dfrac{dy}{dx} = 6x - 18$

$6x - 18 = 0$

$x = 3$

$y = -27$

Coordinates are $(3, -27)$

G 2. $y = x^2 - 32\sqrt{x} = x^2 - 32x^{\frac{1}{2}}$

$\dfrac{dy}{dx} = 2x - 16x^{-\frac{1}{2}} < 0$

$2x - \dfrac{16}{x^{\frac{1}{2}}} < 0$

$2x < \dfrac{16}{x^{\frac{1}{2}}}$

$2x^{\frac{3}{2}} < 16$

$x^{\frac{3}{2}} < 8$

$x < 4$

3. $(2, -3)$

4. $\left(-\frac{1}{3}, \frac{185}{27}\right)$ and $(5, -69)$

5. $f'(x) = 6x + 2x^{-2}$

When $x = 2$, $f'(x) = 6 \times 2 + \frac{2}{4} = 12.5 > 0$ so increasing

50 Stationary points 2

1. (a) Stationary points have coordinates $(3.33, -14.8)$ and $(2, -16)$

(b) $\dfrac{d^2y}{dx^2} = 16 - 6x$

When $x = 2$, $\dfrac{d^2y}{dx^2} = 4 > 0$ so minimum

When $x = 3.33$, $\dfrac{d^2y}{dx^2} = -3.98 < 0$ so maximum

G 2. (a) $y = 6x^{\frac{1}{2}} - 2x^{\frac{3}{2}} + 5$ so $\dfrac{dy}{dx} = 3x^{-\frac{1}{2}} - 3x^{\frac{1}{2}}$

$3x^{-\frac{1}{2}} - 3x^{\frac{1}{2}} = 0$

$3x^{-\frac{1}{2}} = 3x^{\frac{1}{2}}$ so $x = 1$

$y = 6 - 2 + 5 = 9$ Coordinates are $(1, 9)$

(b) $\dfrac{d^2y}{dx^2} = -\frac{3}{2}x^{-\frac{3}{2}} - \frac{3}{2}x^{-\frac{1}{2}}$

(c) At $x = 1$, $\dfrac{d^2y}{dx^2} = -\frac{3}{2} - \frac{3}{2} = -3$; $-3 < 0$ so maximum

3. (a) $x = \sqrt{3}$ or $-\sqrt{3}$

(b) $\dfrac{d^2y}{dx^2} = -72x^{-5}$

At P $x = \sqrt{3}$ $\dfrac{d^2y}{dx^2} = -\dfrac{8\sqrt{3}}{3} < 0$ so maximum

At Q $x = -\sqrt{3}$, $\dfrac{d^2y}{dx^2} = \dfrac{8\sqrt{3}}{3} > 0$ so minimum

51 Max and min problems

G 1. (a) Volume $= 2x^2y = 8000$

$y = \dfrac{8000}{2x^2} = \dfrac{4000}{x^2}$

$A = 2xy + 4xy + 2x^2 = 6xy + 2x^2 = 6x\left(\dfrac{4000}{x^2}\right) + 2x^2$

$= \dfrac{24\,000}{x} + 2x^2$

(b) $A = 24\,000x^{-1} + 2x^2$

$\dfrac{dA}{dx} -24\,000x^{-2} + 4x = 0$ for a stationary point

$4x = 24\,000x^{-2}$

$4x^3 = 24\,000$

$x^3 = 6000$

$x = 18.2$ cm

(c) $\dfrac{d^2A}{dx^2} = 48\,000x^{-3} + 4 = \dfrac{48\,000}{x^3} + 4 = \dfrac{48\,000}{6000} + 4 = 12 > 0$

so minimum

(d) Minimum amount of cardboard $= \dfrac{24\,000}{18.2} + 2(18.2)^2$

$= 1981.2$ cm^2

2. (a) $V = \pi r^2 h$

$A = 2\pi r^2 + 2\pi rh = 900$

$2\pi rh = 900 - 2\pi r^2$

$h = \dfrac{450}{\pi r} - r$

$V = \pi r^2 \left(\dfrac{450}{\pi r} - r\right) = 450r - \pi r^3$

(b) $V = 2073$ cm^3

(c) $r = 6.9$ cm

$\dfrac{d^2V}{dr^2} = -6\pi r = -130 < 0$ so maximum

52 Definite integration

G 1. $\int_1^2 (x^3 - 3x^2 + 5x - 7)\,dx = \left[\dfrac{x^4}{4} - x^3 + \dfrac{5x^2}{2} - 7x\right]_1^2$

$= (4 - 8 + 10 - 14) - \left(\frac{1}{4} - 1 + \frac{5}{2} - 7\right) = -8 - \left(-\frac{21}{4}\right) = -\frac{11}{4}$

G 2. $\int_1^2 \left(2x^2 + 3 - \dfrac{5}{x^2}\right)dx = \int_1^2 (2x^2 + 3 - 5x^{-2})\,dx$

$= \left[\dfrac{2x^3}{3} + 3x + 5x^{-1}\right]_1^2 = \left[\dfrac{2x^3}{3} + 3x + \dfrac{5}{x}\right]_1^2$

$= \left(\frac{16}{3} + 6 + \frac{5}{2}\right) - \left(\frac{2}{3} + 3 + 5\right) = \frac{83}{6} - \frac{26}{3} = \frac{31}{6}$

3. $\frac{47}{2}$

4. $30 + 4\sqrt{2}$

5. $\frac{41}{8}$

53 Area under a curve

G 1. Graph crosses the x-axis at $x = -1$ and $x = 3$

$y = 3 + 2x - x^2$

$\int_{-1}^{3}(3 + 2x - x^2)\,dx = \left[3x + \frac{2x^2}{2} - \frac{x^3}{3}\right]_{-1}^{3} = \left[3x + x^2 - \frac{x^3}{3}\right]_{-1}^{3}$

$= (9 + 9 - 9) - \left(-3 + 1 + \frac{1}{3}\right) = 9 - \left(-\frac{5}{3}\right) = \frac{32}{3}$

Area $= \frac{32}{3}$

G 2. Graph crosses the x-axis at $x = -2$ and $x = 4$

$y = x^2 - 2x - 8$

$\int_{-2}^{4}(x^2 - 2x - 8)\,dx = \left[\frac{x^3}{3} - \frac{2x^2}{2} - 8x\right]_{-2}^{4} = \left[\frac{x^3}{3} - x^2 - 8x\right]_{-2}^{4}$

$= \left(\frac{64}{3} - 16 - 32\right) - \left(-\frac{8}{3} - 4 + 16\right) = -\frac{80}{3} - \frac{28}{3} = -36$

Area $= 36$

3. 24

54 More areas

G 1. $L\,(2, 0)$; $M\,(4, 0)$ At N: $x = 6$, $y = 6^2 - 6 \times 6 + 8 = 8$

Area of triangle $= \frac{1}{2} \times$ base $\times$ height $= \frac{1}{2} \times 4 \times 8 = 16$

$\int_{4}^{6}(x^2 - 6x + 8)\,dx = \left[\frac{x^3}{3} - \frac{6x^2}{2} + 8x\right]_{4}^{6} = \left[\frac{x^3}{3} - 3x^2 + 8x\right]_{4}^{6}$

$= (72 - 108 + 48) - \left(\frac{64}{3} - 48 + 32\right)$

$= 12 - \frac{16}{3} = \frac{20}{3}$

Area of $R = 16 - \frac{20}{3} = \frac{28}{3}$

2. (a) $A\,(-6, 38)$, $B\,(1, 17)$

(b) Area of $S = \frac{385}{2} - 135\frac{1}{3} = \frac{343}{6}$

55 The trapezium rule

G 1. (a)

x	0	0.2	0.4	0.6	0.8	1
y	1	1.23	1.46	**1.70**	**1.96**	2.24

$x = 0.4$: $y = \sqrt{4^{0.4} + 0.4} = 1.463$

$x = 0.6$: $y = \sqrt{4^{0.6} + 0.6} = 1.702$

$x = 0.8$: $y = \sqrt{4^{0.8} + 0.8} = 1.957$

(b) $a = 0$ $b = 1$ $n = 6 - 1 = 5$ $h = \frac{1 - 0}{5} = 0.2$

$\int_{0}^{1}\sqrt{4^x + x}\,dx$

$\approx \frac{1}{2} \times \frac{1}{5}[(1 + 2.24) + 2(1.23 + 1.46 + 1.70 + 1.96)]$

$= 0.1\,(15.94) = 1.59$ (2 d.p.)

2. (a)

x	1	1.1	1.2	1.3	1.4	1.5
y	2.31	**2.50**	2.68	**2.86**	**3.04**	3.21

(b) 1.4

3. (a)

x	2	2.25	2.5	2.75	3
y	2.857	**2.192**	1.739	**1.416**	1.176

(b) 1.84

56–57 You are the examiner!

1. Centre is at midpoint of the diameter, i.e. at $(1, 5)$.

Length of diameter given by

$d^2 = (7 - 3)^2 + (4 + 2)^2 = 16 + 36 = 52$

So $r^2 = 52 \div 4 = 13$

Equation of circle is $(x - 1)^2 + (y - 5)^2 = 13$

2. (a) $a = 1$, $b = \frac{x}{4}$, $n = 10$

$\left(1 + \frac{x}{4}\right)^{10} = 1^{10} + \binom{10}{1}1^9\left(\frac{x}{4}\right) + \binom{10}{2}1^8\left(\frac{x}{4}\right)^2 + \binom{10}{3}1^7\left(\frac{x}{4}\right)^3 + \dots$

$= 1 + \frac{10}{4}x + \frac{10 \times 9}{2 \times 16}x^2 + \frac{10 \times 9 \times 8}{3 \times 2 \times 64}x^3 + \dots$

$= 1 + \frac{5}{2}x + \frac{45}{16}x^2 + \frac{15}{8}x^3 + \dots$

$= 1 + 2.5x + 2.8125x^2 + 1.875x^3 + \dots$

(b) $(1.05)^{10} = \left(1 + \frac{0.2}{4}\right)^{10}$, so $x = 0.2$ and

$(1.05)^{10} \approx 1 + 2.5 \times 0.2 + 2.8125 \times 0.04 + 1.875 \times 0.008$

$= 1 + 0.5 + 0.1125 + 0.015$

$= 1.6275$

3. $20° \leqslant 2x + 20° \leqslant 380°$. Let $Z = 2x + 20°$

$Z = \sin^{-1}(-0.3)$

Principal value is $Z = -17.5°$

so $Z = 360° + (-17.5°) = 342.5°$ $\Rightarrow$ $x = 161.3°$

or $Z = 180° + (17.5°) = 197.5°$ $\Rightarrow$ $x = 88.7°$

4. (a) $\log_2(2x + 10) = \log_2(x - 1)^2 + 1$

$\log_2(2x + 10) - \log_2(x - 1)^2 = \log_2 2$

$\log_2 \frac{(2x + 10)}{(x - 1)^2} = 1$

$\frac{(2x + 10)}{(x - 1)^2} = 2^1$

$2x + 10 = 2(x - 1)^2$

$x + 5 = x^2 - 2x + 1$

$0 = x^2 - 3x - 4$

(b) $x^2 - 3x - 4 = 0$

$(x - 4)(x + 1) = 0$

$x = 4$ or $x = -1$

But $2x + 10$ and $x - 1$ must both be greater than 0,

so $x \neq -1$

Hence $x = 4$

5. At the stationary point, $\frac{dy}{dx} = 0$.

$\frac{dy}{dx} = 8x - 4$

so $8x - 4 = 0$, i.e. $x = \frac{1}{2}$

When $x = \frac{1}{2}$, $y = 4 \times \frac{1}{4} - 4 \times \frac{1}{2} + 5 = 4$

So the stationary point is at $(\frac{1}{2}, 4)$.

Mechanics 1

58 Constant acceleration 1

G 1. (a) $s = ?$ $u = 5$ $v = 20$ $a = ?$ $t = 4$

$v = u + at$

$20 = 5 + a \times 4$ $4a = 15$ $a = 3.75\,\text{m s}^{-2}$

(b) $s = ?$ $u = 5$ $v = 20$ $a = 3.75$ $t = 4$

$s = \frac{1}{2}(5 + 20) \times 4 = 50\,\text{m}$

2. (a) $1.8\,\text{m s}^{-2}$ **(b)** $4.375\,\text{m}$

3. (a) $a = -1.3\,\text{m s}^{-2}$ (deceleration $= 1.3\,\text{m s}^{-2}$)   **(b)** $600\,\text{m}$

59 Constant acceleration 2

G 1.

$t = 0$ $t = 2$ $t = 6$

P Q R

PQ: $s = 45$ $u = u$ $v = ?$ $a = a$ $t = 2$

$45 = u \times 2 + \frac{1}{2}a \times 2^2$ ①

PR: $s = 165$ $u = u$ $v = ?$ $a = a$ $t = 6$

$165 = u \times 6 + \frac{1}{2}a \times 6^2$ ②

$45 = 2u + 2a$ ①

$165 = 6u + 18a$ ②

① $\times$ 3: $135 = 6u + 6a$ ③

② $-$ ③: $30 = 12a$ $a = 2.5\,\text{ms}^{-2}$

Substitute in ①: $45 = 2u + 5$

$2u = 40$

$u = 20\,\text{m s}^{-1}$

2. (a) $37.75\,\text{m s}^{-1}$

(b) $102\,\text{m}$

(c) $6\,\text{s}$

60 Motion under gravity

G 1. (a) $s = ?$ $u = 21$ $v = 0$ $a = -9.8$ $t = ?$
$v^2 = u^2 + 2as \Rightarrow 0^2 = 21^2 - 2 \times 9.8 \times h$ $441 = 19.6h$
$h = 22.5 \approx 23\,\text{m}$ (2 s.f.)

(b) $s = 22.5 + 1.5$ $u = 0$ $v = ?$ $a = -9.8$ $t = ?$
$v^2 = u^2 + 2as \Rightarrow v^2 = 0^2 + 2 \times 9.8 \times 24 = 470.4$
$v = 21.69 \approx 22\,\text{m s}^{-1}$ (2 s.f.)

(c) $s = ?$ $u = 21$ $v = -22$ $a = -9.8$ $t = ?$
$v = u + at$
$-22 = 21 - 9.8t$
$t = 4.39 \approx 4.4\,\text{s}$ (2 s.f.)

G 2. (a) $s = 50$ $u = 0$ $v = ?$ $a = a$ $t = 4$
$s = ut + \tfrac{1}{2}at^2$
$50 = 0 + \tfrac{1}{2}a \times 4^2$ $a = \tfrac{50}{8} = 6.25\,\text{m s}^{-2}$

(b) $v = u + at$
$v = 0 + 6.25 \times 4 = 25\,\text{m s}^{-1}$

(c) $s = ut + \tfrac{1}{2}at^2$
$s = 25 \times 3 - \tfrac{1}{2} \times 9.8 \times 9 = 30.9$
Total height $= 30.9 + 50 = 80.9 \approx 81\,\text{m}$ (2 s.f.)

61 Speed–time graphs

G 1. (a)

(b) Area = Area 1 + Area 2 + Area 3
Area $= (30 \times 40) + (20 \times 60) + (\tfrac{1}{2} \times 10 \times x) = 2500$
$1200 + 1200 + 5x = 2500$
$x = \tfrac{100}{5} = 20$
Deceleration $= \tfrac{10}{20} = 0.5\,\text{m s}^{-2}$

2. (a)

(b) $80\,\text{m}$

(c) $35\,\text{s}$

62 Other motion graphs

G 1. $a = \tfrac{25}{10} = 2.5$ ① $a = 0$ ② $a = \tfrac{-25}{5} = -5$ ③

G 2. (a)

(b) $T = 8.75\,\text{s}$

(c)

63 Forces

G 1. (a) $2750 - 900 - 250 = (2500 + 1500)a$
$1600 = 4000a$
$a = 0.4\,\text{m s}^{-2}$

(b)
$T - 250 = 1500a$
$T = 600 + 250$
$T = 850\,\text{N}$

2. (a) $T = 12\,608 \approx 13\,000\,\text{N}$ (2 s.f.)

(b) $R = 663 \approx 660\,\text{N}$ (2 s.f.)

64 Resolving forces

G 1. (a) $v^2 = u^2 + 2as$
$14^2 = 20^2 + 2 \times a \times 100$
$a = -1.02$
Deceleration $= 1.02\,\text{m s}^{-2}$

(b) $T\cos\theta - 300 = 750 \times -1.02$
$0.9T = 300 - 765$
$T = -465 \div 0.9 = -516.66...$
Force $= 517\,\text{N}$

(c) $-T\cos\theta - 500 - R = 1750 \times -1.02$
$517 \times 0.9 - 500 + 1785 = R$
$R = 1750\,\text{N}$

2. (a) $a = 4.9\,\text{m s}^{-2}$

(b) $42\,\text{N}$

65 Friction

G 1. (a) $R(\rightarrow)$: $160\cos 20° - F = 0$
$F = 150.35\,\text{N}$
$F = \mu R = 0.3R$, so $R = 501\,\text{N}$

(b) $R(\uparrow)$: $R + 160\sin 20° - mg = 0$
$501.16 + 54.72 = m \times 9.8$
$555.88 = 9.8m$
$m = 56.7 \approx 57\,\text{kg}$ (2 s.f.)

2. $P = 871 \approx 870\,\text{N}$ (2 s.f.)

66 Sloping planes

G 1. (a) $R(\searrow)$: $R - 4g\cos 30° = 0$
$R = 33.95 \approx 34\,\text{N}$ (2 s.f.)

(b) $R(\nearrow)$: $40 - 4g\sin 30° - F = 4a$
$F = \mu R = 0.5 \times 33.95 = 16.975$; $40 - 19.6 - 16.975 = 4a$
$a = 0.856 \approx 0.86\,\text{m s}^{-2}$ (2 s.f.)

2. (a) $a = 1.25\,\text{m s}^{-2}$

(b) $\mu = 0.278 \approx 0.28$ (2 s.f.)

3. (a) $R = 32.36 \approx 32\,\text{N}$ (2 s.f.)

(b) $\mu = 0.644 \approx 0.64$ (2 s.f.)

67 Pulleys

1. (a) A: $4g - T = 4a$

$$4g - \frac{16g}{7} = T$$

$$T = \frac{12g}{7} \, (= 16.8 \approx 17\,\text{N})$$

(b) B: $T - mg = ma$

$$\frac{12g}{7} = m\left(g + \frac{4g}{7}\right)$$

$$\frac{12g}{7} = \frac{11mg}{7}$$

$$m = 1.1\,\text{kg}$$

(c) $(\uparrow)$: $v = u + at = 0 + \frac{4g}{7} \times 0.5 = \frac{2g}{7} = 2.8\,\text{m}\,\text{s}^{-1}$

$(\uparrow)$: $s = ut + \frac{1}{2}at^2 = 0 + \frac{1}{2} \times \frac{4g}{7} \times 0.5^2 = 0.7$

$(\downarrow)$: $s = ut + \frac{1}{2}at^2 = 0.7 + 3 = 3.7$

$3.7 = -2.8t + 4.9t^2$

$4.9t^2 - 2.8t - 3.7 = 0$

$$t = \frac{2.8 \pm \sqrt{2.8^2 + 4 \times 4.9 \times 3.7}}{9.8}$$

$$= 1.2\,\text{s}$$

2. (a) $T = \dfrac{32mg}{5}$

(b) $k = 16$

68 Connected particles 1

1. (a) Q: $5g - T = 5a$ ①

P: $R = 4g\cos 40° = 30\,\text{N}$

$T - F - 4g\sin 40° = 4a$ ②

$T - 0.4 \times 30 - 25.2 = 4a$

$T - 37.2 = 4a$ ③

① + ②: $5g - 37.2 = 9a$

$11.8 = 9a$

$a = 1.31 \approx 1.3\,\text{m}\,\text{s}^{-2}$ (2 s.f.)

(b) From ③: $T - 37.2 = 4 \times 1.31$

$T = 42.44 \approx 42\,\text{N}$ (2 s.f.)

(c) $s = 0.6$ $u = 0$ $a = 1.31$

$v^2 = u^2 + 2as = 0 + 2 \times 1.31 \times 0.6$

$v = 1.25 \approx 1.3\,\text{m}\,\text{s}^{-1}$ (2 s.f.)

2. (a) $a = 0.4g$ (b) $T = 3.6mg$

69 Connected particles 2

1. (a) (i) P: $T - 5g\sin\alpha = 5a$ ①

Scale pan: $15g - T = 15a$ ②

① + ②: $15g - 3g = 20a$

$a = 0.6g$

(ii) Substitute in ①: $T - 3g = 3g \Rightarrow T = 6g$

(b) Q: $5g - N = 5 \times 0.6g$

$5g - N = 3g \Rightarrow N = 2g$

(c) $F = T\cos\left(\dfrac{90 - \alpha}{2}\right) + T\cos\left(\dfrac{90 - \alpha}{2}\right)$

$\alpha = \sin^{-1}\left(\frac{3}{5}\right) = 36.9°$

$F = 2 \times 6g\cos\left(\dfrac{90 - 36.9}{2}\right) = 105 \approx 110\,\text{N}$ (2 s.f.)

2. (a) $m = 2.04 \approx 2.0\,\text{kg}$ (2 s.f.)

(b) $18\,\text{N}$

70 Collisions and momentum

1. (a) $3 \times 4 + 3.5 \times (-5) = 3 \times (-1.5) + 3.5 \times v$

$12 - 17.5 = -4.5 + 3.5v$

$v = -0.286\,\text{m}\,\text{s}^{-1}$ so speed $= 0.286\,\text{m}\,\text{s}^{-1}$

(b) Direction of Q is unchanged.

2. $m = 3.375\,\text{kg}$

3. $m = 3000\,\text{kg}$

71 Impulse

1. (a) $0.8 \times 9 + 0.4 \times (-3) = 0.8 \times v + 1.2 \times v$

$7.2 - 1.2 = 2v \Rightarrow v = 3\,\text{m}\,\text{s}^{-1}$

(b) $I = mv - mu = 0.4 \times 9 - 0.4 \times (-3) = 3.6 + 1.2$

$= 4.8\,\text{N}\,\text{s}$

2. (a) $8\,\text{m}\,\text{s}^{-1}$ (b) $4\,\text{m}\,\text{s}^{-1}$

72 Static particles

1. (a) $R(\rightarrow)$: $T\cos\alpha = 5$ $\tan\alpha = \frac{3}{4}$ so $\cos\alpha = \frac{4}{5}$ $\sin\alpha = \frac{3}{5}$

$T \times \frac{4}{5} = 5 \Rightarrow T = \frac{25}{4}\,\text{N}$

(b) $R(\uparrow)$: $T + T\sin\alpha = W$

$\frac{25}{4} + \frac{25}{4} \times \frac{3}{5} = W \Rightarrow W = 10\,\text{N}$

2. (a) $T = 41.2\,\text{N}$ (b) $m = 4.475 \approx 4.5\,\text{kg}$ (2 s.f.)

3. $\alpha = 56°$, $T = 35.6 \approx 36\,\text{N}$ (2 s.f.)

73 Limiting equilibrium

1. (a) $R(\searrow)$: $P\sin 20 + 15\cos 20 = 20$

$P\sin 20 + 14.10 = 20$

$P = 17.3\,\text{N}$

(b) $R(\nearrow)$: $P\cos 20 = 15\sin 20 + F$

$17.3\cos 20 - 15\sin 20 = \mu \times 20$

$\mu = 0.56$

(c) $R = 15\cos 20 = 14.10\,\text{N}$

$F_{max} = 0.56 \times 14.10 = 7.90\,\text{N}$

Component of weight down the plane $= 15\sin 20$

$= 5.13\,\text{N}$

$5.13 < 7.90$ so parcel will not move

2. $180\,\text{N}$

74 Moments 1

1. (a) $\circlearrowright$ moment about $C = 2400 \times 0.4$

$\circlearrowleft$ moment about $C = 150 \times 1.6 + F \times 3.6$

$960 = 3.6F + 240$

$F = 200\,\text{N}$

(b) $\circlearrowright$ moment about $C = 2400 \times d$

$\circlearrowleft$ moment about $C = 150 \times (2 - d) + 150 \times (4 - d)$

$2400d = 300 - 150d + 600 - 150d$

$2700d = 900$

$d = 33\,\text{cm}$ to nearest cm

2. (a) $R = 637 \approx 640\,\text{N}$ (2 s.f.)

(b) distance $= 1.28 \approx 1.3\,\text{m}$ (2 s.f.)

75 Moments 2

1. (a) $R(\uparrow)$: $T + 4T = 70g$

$T = 14g = 137.2\,\text{N}$

so $4T = 548.8$

$\approx 550\,\text{N}$ (2 s.f.)

(b) $\circlearrowright$ moment about $C = T \times (4 - x) + 25g \times x$

$= 137.2(4 - x) + 245x$

$\circlearrowleft$ moment about $C = 45g \times (2 - x) = 441(2 - x)$

$548.8 - 137.2x + 245x = 882 - 441x$

$548.8x = 333.2$

$x = 0.607\,\text{m} \approx 61\,\text{cm}$ (2 s.f.)

2. tension $= 300\,\text{N}$, weight $= 700\,\text{N}$

76 Centres of mass

1. (a) ↺ moment about D: 1750×6.5
   ↻ moment about D: $W \times 2.5$
   $2.5W = 11\,375 \Rightarrow W = 4550\,\text{N}$

   (b) ↺ moment about D: 1750×6.5
   ↻ moment about C: $W \times x$
   ↻ moment about D: $W \times (5 - x)$
   ↺ moment about C: 1500×6.5
   $11\,375 = 5W - Wx$
   $9750 = Wx$
   $21\,125 = 5W$
   $W = 4225\,\text{N}$

2. (a) ↺ moment about D: $180 \times 3.5 = 240(6 - x) + W \times 6$
   $630 = 1440 - 240x + 6W$
   $240x - 6W = 810$
   $40x - W = 135$

   (b) $x = 4.7\,\text{m}$, $W = 53\,\text{N}$

77 Vectors

1. (a) $\mathbf{r} = \mathbf{r_0} + \mathbf{v}t$
   $7\mathbf{i} + 10\mathbf{j} = (2\mathbf{i} - 5\mathbf{j}) + \mathbf{v} \times 2.5$
   $5\mathbf{i} + 15\mathbf{j} = 2.5\mathbf{v}$ $\mathbf{v} = 2\mathbf{i} + 6\mathbf{j}$
   $v = \sqrt{4 + 36} = \sqrt{40} = 6.32\,\text{m s}^{-1}$

   (b) $b = 2\mathbf{i} - 5\mathbf{j} + (2\mathbf{i} + 6\mathbf{j})t$

2. Distance = 13 m

3. (a) $\mathbf{v} = 4\mathbf{i} + 6\mathbf{j}$

   (b) $p = (12\mathbf{i} + 14\mathbf{j}) + (4\mathbf{i} + 6\mathbf{j})t$
   $q = (8\mathbf{i} - 4\mathbf{j}) + 10t\mathbf{j}$

   (c) $\overrightarrow{PQ} = q - p = (-4\mathbf{i} - 18\mathbf{j}) + (-4\mathbf{i} + 4\mathbf{j})t$
   $= (-4 - 4t)\mathbf{i} + (-18 + 4t)\mathbf{j}$
   $d^2 = (-4 - 4t)^2 + (-18 + 4t)^2$
   $= 32t^2 - 112t + 340$

78 Vectors and bearings

1. (a)

   $\tan\theta = \frac{2}{5} = 0.4$ $\theta = 21.8 \approx 22°$
   Bearing = $360° - 22° = 338°$

   (b) Position vector of A at time t = $(4\mathbf{i} - 7\mathbf{j}) + (-2\mathbf{i} + 5\mathbf{j})t$
   $= (4 - 2t)\mathbf{i} + (-7 + 5t)\mathbf{j}$
   Position vector of B at time t = $(-20\mathbf{i} + 5\mathbf{j}) + (2\mathbf{i} + 3\mathbf{j})t$
   $= (-20 + 2t)\mathbf{i} + (5 + 3t)\mathbf{j}$
   i components equal: $4 - 2t = -20 + 2t$ $t = 6\,\text{s}$
   j components at $t = 6$: $A: -7 + 30 = 23$
   $B: 5 + 18 = 23$
   Position vector of P: $-8\mathbf{i} + 23\mathbf{j}$

2. (a) $108°$
   (b) $r = 20\mathbf{i} - 20\mathbf{j}$
   (c) $s = (16 + 6t)\mathbf{i} - 8\mathbf{j}$
   (d) 1440

79 Forces as vectors

1. (a) $16\mathbf{i} - 6\mathbf{j} = (4\mathbf{i} + 3\mathbf{j}) + 5\mathbf{a}$
   $5\mathbf{a} = 12\mathbf{i} - 9\mathbf{j}$, giving $\mathbf{a} = 2.4\mathbf{i} - 1.8\mathbf{j}$

   (b) $\mathbf{F} = 5(2.4\mathbf{i} - 1.8\mathbf{j}) = 12\mathbf{i} - 9\mathbf{j}$
   $|\mathbf{F}| = \sqrt{12^2 + 9^2} = \sqrt{225} = 15\,\text{N}$

2. (a) $67°$ (b) $7.8\,\text{N}$
   (c) $\mathbf{v} = (10\mathbf{i} - 5\mathbf{j}) + 4(5\mathbf{i} + 12\mathbf{j}) = 30\mathbf{i} + 43\mathbf{j}$

3. (a) $\mathbf{F} = 6\mathbf{i} - 9\mathbf{j}$ (b) $t = 2\,\text{s}$

80 Vectors and resultants

1. (a)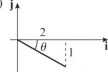

   $\tan\theta = \frac{1}{2}$; $\theta = 26.6°$
   angle = $90 + 26.6 = 116.6° \approx 117°$ (3 s.f.)

   (b) $\mathbf{R} = (3\mathbf{i} - 6\mathbf{j}) + (p\mathbf{i} + q\mathbf{j})$
   $= (3 + p)\mathbf{i} + (-6 + q)\mathbf{j}$
   $3 + p = -2(-6 + q)$
   $3 + p = 12 - 2q$
   $p + 2q = 9$

   (c) $p + 2q = 9$ $q = 2$ $p + 4 = 9$ $p = 5$
   $\mathbf{R} = 8\mathbf{i} - 4\mathbf{j}$ $|\mathbf{R}| = \sqrt{8^2 + 4^2} = \sqrt{60}$
   $\sqrt{60} = m \times 4\sqrt{5}$
   $m = \frac{\sqrt{60}}{4\sqrt{5}} = \frac{\sqrt{3}}{2}\,\text{kg}$

2. (a) $63°$ (b) $p = -2$

3. (a) $9\mathbf{i} - 3\mathbf{j}$ (b) $3\mathbf{i} - \mathbf{j}$ (c) $6.08\,\text{m s}^{-1}$

81 Modelling assumptions

1. (a) If the plane is smooth you can ignore friction.
   (b) If the string is light it has no weight.
   (c) If the string is inextensible the magnitude of the acceleration is the same for both particles.
   (d) If the pulley is smooth the tension in the string is the same on both sides of the pulley.
   (e) If A and B are modelled as particles their weights act at a single point.

2. If the ball moves freely under gravity you can ignore air resistance and assume the acceleration is constant.

3. (a) If the rod is uniform the weight acts at the midpoint.
   (b) In equilibrium the resultant force in any direction is zero.
   (c) If the loads are modelled as particles their weights act at a single point.
   (d) If the cables are modelled as light inextensible strings they have no weight and the tension is the same throughout the cables.

82–83 You are the examiner!

1. (a) $s = 28.9$ $u = u$ $v = 0$ $a = -9.8$
   $v^2 = u^2 + 2as$
   $0 = u^2 - 2 \times 9.8 \times 28.9$
   $u^2 = 2 \times 9.8 \times 28.9$
   $u = \sqrt{566.44}$
   $= 23.8\,\text{m s}^{-1}$

   (b) $s = ut + \frac{1}{2}at^2$
   $-2.5 = 23.8T - \frac{1}{2} \times 9.8T^2$
   $4.9T^2 - 23.8T - 2.5 = 0$
   $T = \dfrac{23.8 \pm \sqrt{23.8^2 + 4 \times 4.9 \times 2.5}}{9.8}$
   $= 4.96 \approx 5.0\,\text{s}$ (1 d.p.)

2. (a) $R = 3.5 \times 9.8 \cos 15° = 33.1 \approx 33\,\text{N}$ (2 s.f.)

(b) $F = 0.5 \times 33.1 = 16.6\,\text{N}$

   $F + 3.5 \times 9.8 \sin 15° = X$

   $16.6 + 8.88 = 25.4 \approx 25\,\text{N}$ (2 s.f.)

(c) $F_{max} = 16.6\,\text{N}$

   $3.5 \times 9.8 \sin 15° = 8.88$ (component of weight down plane = 8.88 N)

   Component of weight down plane is less than F_{max}, so P will remain in equilibrium.

3. (a) $v = u + at$

   $= (-3\mathbf{i} + 6\mathbf{j}) + (3\mathbf{i} - 2\mathbf{j})t$

   $= (-3 + 3t)\mathbf{i} + (6 - 2t)\mathbf{j}$

   $(6 - 2t) = 0$, $t = 3$

(b) $t = 4$: $v = (-3 + 12)\mathbf{i} + (6 - 8)\mathbf{j}$

   $= 9\mathbf{i} - 2\mathbf{j}$

   speed $= \sqrt{81 + 4} = \sqrt{85} = 9.22\,\text{m s}^{-1}$

4. (a) $0.4u = -3 \times 0.4 + 6 \times 0.7$

   $= -1.2 + 4.2 = 3$

   $u = 7.5\,\text{m s}^{-1}$

(b) $I = 0.7 \times 6 = 4.2\,\text{N s}$

(c) $u = 6 \qquad v = 0 \qquad t = 1.5$

   $v = u + at$

   $0 = 6 + 1.5a \Rightarrow a = -4\,\text{m s}^{-1}$

   $R = 0.7 \times 4 = 2.8\,\text{N}$

Statistics 1

84 Mean

1. (a) $93.4\,\text{g}$ (1 d.p.)

(b) $94.2\,\text{g}$ (1 d.p.)

2. (a) The midpoint of the 6–12 minutes group is 9 minutes. The midpoint of the 13–20 minutes group is 16.5 minutes.

(b) $\bar{x} = \dfrac{\Sigma fx}{\Sigma f} = \dfrac{6 \times 3 + 11 \times 9 + 7 \times 16.5 + 8 \times 25.5}{32}$

   $= \dfrac{436.5}{32} = 13.6$ minutes (1 d.p.)

3. $14.2\,\text{km}$ (1 d.p.)

85 Median and quartiles

1. (a) 28

(b) $n = 23 \qquad \dfrac{n}{2} = 11.5$, Q_2 (median) = 12th value

   = 23 lessons

   For Q_1, work out $23 \div 4 = 5.75 \rightarrow$ 6th value

   = 14 lessons

   For Q_3, work out $3 \times 23 \div 4 = 17.25 \rightarrow$ 18th value

   = 32 lessons

2. (a) 18

(b) $Q_1 = 24$, $Q_2 = 36$, $Q_3 = 52$

3. (a) 27

(b) $Q_1 = 25.5$, $Q_2 = 31.5$, $Q_3 = 44.5$

86 Linear interpolation

1. $\dfrac{n}{2} = 135$, so the median is $(135 - 29) = 106$ values into the $10 \le w < 15$ group.

   This group is 5 kg wide so each member is worth $\frac{5}{121}$ kg

   $Q_2 = 10 + 106 \times \frac{5}{121}$ kg $= 14.380\,16... = 14.4$ kg (1 d.p.)

2. $Q_1 = 34.1$, $Q_2 = 47.2$, $Q_3 = 57.7$ (1 d.p.)

3. $Q_1 = 17$, $Q_2 = 32$, $Q_3 = 49.9$ (1 d.p.)

87 Standard deviation 1

1. Variance $= \dfrac{\Sigma x^2}{n} - \left(\dfrac{\Sigma x}{n}\right)^2 = \left(\dfrac{27\,872}{27}\right) - \left(\dfrac{768}{27}\right)^2$

   $= 1032.29... - (28.44\,...)^2 = 223.209...$

   Standard deviation $= \sqrt{223.209...} = 14.9402...$

   $= 14.9$ books (3 s.f.)

2. 15.6 years (3 s.f.)

3. 6.19 letters (3 s.f.)

88 Standard deviation 2

1. $\Sigma f = 160$

   $\Sigma fx = 12 \times 5 + 27 \times 12.5 + 85 \times 22.5 + 36 \times 40 = 3750$

   $\Sigma fx^2 = 12 \times 5^2 + 27 \times 12.5^2 + 85 \times 22.5^2 + 36 \times 40^2$

   $= 105\,150$

   Variance $= \dfrac{105\,150}{160} - \left(\dfrac{3750}{160}\right)^2 = 107.871...$

   Standard deviation $= \sqrt{(107.871...)} = 10.386...$

   $= 10.4$ minutes (3 s.f.)

2. £0.873 million (3 s.f.)

3. (a) 38 mm and 70.5 mm

(b) 25.2 mm (3 s.f.)

89 Box plots and outliers

1. $\text{IQR} = 40 - 28 = 12$

   $1.25 \times \text{IQR} = 1.25 \times 12 = 15$

   $Q_3 + 15 = 40 + 15 = 55$

   $Q_1 - 15 = 28 - 15 = 13$

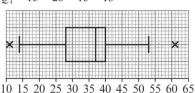

2. (a) (i) 28   (ii) Lower quartile

(b) $\text{IQR} = 36 - 28 = 8$, $28 - 1.5 \times 8 = 28 - 12 = 16$; 10 is less than this value so is an outlier.

3.

   $\text{IQR} = 10 \quad Q_3 + 15 = 36 + 15 = 51 \quad Q_1 - 15 = 26 - 15 = 11$

   Outliers at 7, 9 and 53

90 Histograms

1. Frequency for $0 < t \le 10$ class $= 2.8 \times 10 = 28$

   Frequency for $10 < t \le 30$ class $= 2 \times 20 = 40$

Time, t (minutes)	Number of cars
$0 < t \le 10$	28
$10 < t \le 30$	40
$30 < t \le 60$	48
$60 < t \le 80$	16

2. (a) Frequency density (height of bar) for $20 < v \le 30$ is 11

   The frequency for the $45 < v \le 50$ group is 110

(b) 335 cars

3. Width = 2 cm, height = 1.5 cm

91 Skewness

G 1. For data set A: $Q_2 - Q_1 = 14 - 10 = 4$

$$Q_3 - Q_2 = 21 - 14 = 7$$

So, $Q_2 - Q_1 < Q_3 - Q_2$ and data set A is positively skew.
(There is a significant gap between the upper quartile and the highest value which emphasises the positive skew.)

For data set B: $Q_2 - Q_1 = 30 - 23 = 7$

$$Q_3 - Q_2 = 35 - 30 = 5$$

So, $Q_2 - Q_1 > Q_3 - Q_2$ and data set B is negatively skew.
(There is a significant gap between the lower quartile and the lowest value which emphasises the negative skew.)

For data set C: $Q_2 - Q_1 = 22 - 17 = 5$

$$Q_3 - Q_2 = 28 - 22 = 6$$

So, $Q_2 - Q_1 < Q_3 - Q_2$. But 5 and 6 are almost equal; very slight positive skew.

(The gap between the upper quartile and the highest value is very similar to the gap between the lower quartile and the lowest value. Also, the median is almost exactly halfway between the lowest value and the highest value. This suggests the data has very slight skew.)

2. Using $\dfrac{3(\text{mean} - \text{median})}{\text{standard deviation}}$

For data set D: $-0.5647...$ Slight negative skew

For data set E: $-3.2903...$ Negative skew

For data set F: $2.7567...$ Positive skew

3. (a) $Q_2 - Q_1 = 161 - 154 = 7$ and $Q_3 - Q_2 = 168 - 161 = 7$, which suggests no skew.

(b) Standard deviation = $8.0144...$

$$\dfrac{3(\text{mean} - \text{median})}{\text{standard deviation}} = 0.510\,44...$$

supporting no skew in (a).

92 Comparing distributions

G 1. The median for the boys' marks (52) is less than the median for the girls' marks (60), so the boys did less well overall.

The IQR for the boys was 20 compared with 30 for the girls so the boys' marks were more closely grouped than the girls' marks.

Only 25% of the boys scored more than 58, whereas 50% of the girls scored more than 60.

The marks for both show negative skew.

For the boys, $Q_2 - Q_1 = 14$ and $Q_3 - Q_2 = 6$.

For the girls, $Q_2 - Q_1 = 24$ and $Q_3 - Q_2 = 6$.

2. (a) For Duckford, $Q_1 = 21$, $Q_2 = 33$, $Q_3 = 41$

(b) For Duckford,

(i) mean = 31.62

(ii) standard deviation = 13.01

(c) The mean for Duckford (31.62) is greater than the mean for Swanthorpe (24.71), so the residents of Duckford received, on average, more junk mail. The greater median for Duckford supports this.

The standard deviations are very similar (13.01 and 12.21) but the IQR for Duckford is 20 compared with an IQR of 14 for Swanthorpe, so the data for Swanthorpe is more closely grouped than the data for Duckford.

For Duckford, $Q_2 - Q_1 = 12$ and $Q_3 - Q_2 = 8$, suggesting negative skew.

For Swanthorpe, $Q_2 - Q_1 = 7$ and $Q_3 - Q_2 = 7$, suggesting no skew.

93 Drawing Venn diagrams

G 1. (a) The 11 children who had a cat and a dog include the 2 children who had all three pets.

So $11 - 2 = 9$ children had a cat and a dog but not a rabbit. This is $C \cap D \cap R'$.

The 7 children who had a cat and a rabbit include the 2 children who had all three pets.

So $7 - 2 = 5$ children had a cat and a rabbit but not a dog. This is $C \cap R \cap D'$.

Similarly, $5 - 2 = 3$ is the number for the region $D \cap R \cap C'$.

The total number who had a cat is 31, but $9 + 5 + 2 = 16$ of these have already been counted, leaving $31 - 16 = 15$ as the number in the 'cat only' region.

Similarly 'dog only' $= 35 - (9 + 3 + 2) = 21$, and 'rabbit only' $= 18 - (5 + 3 + 2) = 8$.

The final calculation is to add up all the numbers found so far and subtract from 80 to find out how many people had none of these three pets.
$80 - (15 + 21 + 8 + 9 + 5 + 3 + 2) = 17$

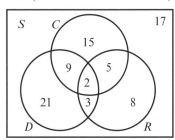

(b) Children who did not have a cat or a dog = 25

2. (a)

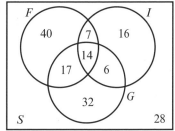

(b) The number who had been to exactly two of the three countries = $17 + 7 + 6 = 30$

94 Using Venn diagrams

G 1. (a) The total number of students =
$21 + 4 + 12 + 6 + 15 + 22 = 80$

The number taking only one subject =
$21 + 12 + 15 = 48$

So the probability is $\dfrac{48}{80} = \dfrac{3 \times 16}{5 \times 16} = \dfrac{3}{5}$

(b) The number of students taking Maths or English or both $= 21 + 4 + 12 + 6 = 43$

So probability $= \dfrac{43}{80}$

2. (a)

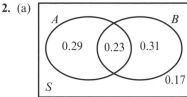

(b) $P(A) = 0.52$

$P(A' \cap B) = 0.31$

3. (a)

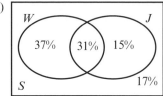

(b) P(W or J but not both) = 0.37 + 0.15 = 0.52

95 Conditional probability

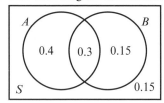 1. (a) The number choosing choc-chip = 10 + 8 + 3 + 4 = 25

Of these 25, 3 + 4 = 7 choose toffee, so the probability = $\frac{7}{25}$

(b) The number choosing vanilla or toffee = 5 + 2 + 8 + 3 + 4 + 9 = 31

Of these 31, 8 + 3 + 4 = 15 choose choc-chip, so the probability = $\frac{15}{31}$

2. (a) $\frac{11}{46}$ (b) $\frac{18}{39}$ (c) $\frac{9}{34}$

96 Probability formulae

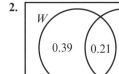 1. This Venn diagram summarises the following answers.

(a) P($A' \cap B'$) = 1 − P($A \cup B$) = 1 − 0.85 = 0.15

(b) P($A \cap B$) = P(A) + P(B) − P($A \cup B$)
= 0.7 + 0.45 − 0.85 = 0.3

(c) $A \cap B'$ is the region within A but outside B.
P($A \cap B'$) = 0.7 − 0.3 = 0.4

(d) $A' \cup B$ is the region outside A but including all of B (the whole sample space, except the region in part (c)).
P($A' \cup B$) = 1 − P($A \cap B'$) = 1 − 0.4 = 0.6

2.

(a) P($C \cap W$) = 0.21

(b) P($W' \cap C'$) = 0.12

(c) P($C \mid W'$) = 0.7

97 Independent events

1. (a) $q + r$

(b) $q + r - qr$

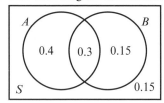 2. Total number of people = 7 + 4 + 9 + 2 + 3 + 2 + 5 + 8 = 40

$$P(C) = \frac{7 + 4 + 2 + 3}{40} = \frac{16}{40} = \frac{2}{5}$$

$$P(G) = \frac{5 + 2 + 2 + 3}{40} = \frac{12}{40} = \frac{3}{10}$$

$$P(C \cap G) = \frac{2 + 3}{40} = \frac{5}{40} = \frac{1}{8}$$

$$P(C) \times P(G) = \frac{2}{5} \times \frac{3}{10} = \frac{6}{50} = \frac{3}{25}$$

$\frac{1}{8} \neq \frac{3}{25}$ so the events are not independent

3. (a) P(A) = $\frac{17}{25}$ (b) P($A \cap B$) = $\frac{51}{200}$

(c) P($A \cap B'$) = $\frac{17}{40}$ (d) P($A' \mid B$) = $\frac{8}{25}$

98 Tree diagrams

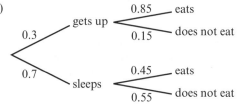 1. (a)

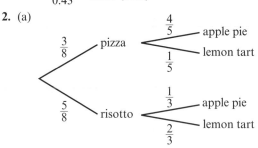

(b) P(does not eat) = 0.3 × 0.15 + 0.7 × 0.55
= 0.045 + 0.385 = 0.43

(c) P(gets up immediately | does not eat)

$$= \frac{P(\text{gets up immediately and does not eat})}{P(\text{does not eat})}$$

$$= \frac{0.045}{0.43} = 0.105 \text{ (3 s.f.)}$$

2. (a)

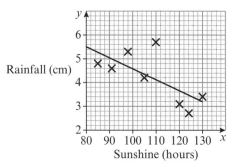

(b) P(Keisha eats either risotto or lemon tart, but not both) = $\frac{17}{60}$

(c) P(Keisha ate pizza | Keisha eats apple pie) = $\frac{36}{61}$

99 Correlation

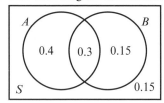 1. (a) $S_{hh} = \Sigma h^2 - \frac{(\Sigma h)^2}{n} = 356\,899 - \frac{(2067)^2}{12} = 858.25$

$S_{ww} = \Sigma w^2 - \frac{(\Sigma w)^2}{n} = 72\,520 - \frac{(922)^2}{12} = 1679.66$

$S_{hw} = \Sigma hw - \frac{(\Sigma h)(\Sigma w)}{n} = 159\,555 - \frac{(2067)(922)}{12} = 740.5$

(b) $r = \frac{S_{hw}}{\sqrt{S_{hh} \times S_{ww}}} = \frac{740.5}{\sqrt{858.25 \times 1679.66}} = 0.617 \text{ (3 s.f.)}$

2. (a) $\Sigma x = 664$ $\Sigma y = 607$ $S_{xx} = 1348.4$
$S_{yy} = 1640.1$ $S_{xy} = 1240.2$

(b) $r = 0.834$ (3 s.f.)

100 Understanding the PMCC

1. Set A: 0.45 because it shows positive correlation which is not very strong.

Set B: −0.91, because it shows fairly strong negative correlation.

Set C: −0.16 because it shows neither positive nor negative correlation, so the correlation coefficient must be near 0.

2. (a)

Rainfall (cm)

Sunshine (hours)

(b) $r = -0.689$ (3 s.f.)

(c) There is weak negative linear correlation. As the hours of sunshine increase the rainfall decreases.

101 Regression lines

1. (a) $\bar{x} = \frac{268}{8} = 33.5$ and $\bar{y} = \frac{252}{8} = 31.5$

   $b = \frac{S_{xy}}{S_{xx}} = \frac{414}{598} = 0.692$ (3 s.f.) and

   $a = \bar{y} - b\bar{x} = 31.5 - 0.692 \times 33.5 = 8.31$ (3 s.f.)

   Equation is $y = 8.31 + 0.692x$

   (b) x is the independent variable. The maths scores are controlled and the science scores are considered relative to them.

   (c) $r = 0.828$, which is close to 1, indicating good positive linear correlation.

2. (a) $S_{xy} = 458.89 - \frac{72 \times 66.3}{10} = -18.47$

   (b) $b = \frac{-18.47}{20.62} = -0.896$ (3 s.f.) and

   $a = 6.63 - (-0.896) \times 7.2 = 13.1$

   Equation is $y = 13.1 - 0.896x$

   (c) $r = -0.899$, which is very close to -1, indicating strong negative linear correlation.

102 Using regression lines

1. (a) $\bar{x} = \frac{236}{20} = 11.8$ and $\bar{y} = \frac{374}{20} = 18.7$

   $b = \frac{S_{xy}}{S_{xx}} = \frac{4140.2}{3136.4} = 1.32$ (3 s.f.)

   and $a = \bar{y} - b\bar{x} = 18.7 - 1.32 \times 11.8 = 3.12$ (3 s.f.)

   Equation is $y = 3.12 + 1.32x$

   (b) $a = £3.12$ is the fixed charge – the price on the taxi meter at the start of the journey.

   $b = £1.32$ is the cost per mile of the journey.

2. (a) $y = -88.7 + 3.01v$

   (b) (i) 273 m (3 s.f.)   (ii) 363 m (3 s.f.)

   (c) The 273 estimate will be reliable because the 120 km/h speed is within the range of the given data.

   The answer fits well with the adjacent values for 110 km/h and 130 km/h.

   The 363 value is unreliable because the speed of 150 km/h is outside the given range. There is no evidence that a linear relationship will continue.

   (d) $r = 0.983$ (3 s.f.)

   (e) The value of 0.983 indicates a very strong positive linear correlation between the speed of the car and the braking distance.

103 Coding

1. (a)

x	1	3	5	8	10	12
u	0	1.2	2.6	5	6.9	9

   (b) $\Sigma u = 24.7$ $\Sigma u^2 = 161.81$

   (c) $\bar{u} = 24.7 \div 6 = 4.1166... = 4.12$ (3 s.f.)

   Variance for $u = \frac{\Sigma u^2}{n} - (\bar{u})^2 = \frac{161.81}{6} - (4.1166...)^2$

   $= 10.021...$

   Standard deviation $= \sqrt{(10.021...)} = 3.1656...$

   $= 3.17$ (3 s.f.)

   (d) Mean for $p = 1000\bar{u} + 14\,000 = 1000(4.1166...) + 14\,000$

   $= 18\,116.6... = £18\,117$

   Standard deviation for $p = 1000 \times$ SD for $u = 3165.66...$

   $= £3166$

2. (a) Regression equation is $u = 19.8 - 1.29x$

   (b) When $x = 6$, $u = 12.06$, so $t = 5u + 100 = 160.3$ s

   (c) $r = -0.977$ (r for x and t is the same value as r for x and u)

104 Random variables

1. (a) $P(X = 1) = k \times 1^2 = k$ $P(X = 2) = k \times 2^2 = 4k$

   $P(X = 3) = k \times 3^2 = 9k$ $P(X = 4) = 3 \times k \times 4 = 12k$

   $k + 4k + 9k + 12k = 1$, giving $k = \frac{1}{26}$

x	1	2	3	4
$P(X = x)$	$\frac{1}{26}$	$\frac{4}{26}$	$\frac{9}{26}$	$\frac{12}{26}$

   (b) $P(X < 3) = \frac{1}{26} + \frac{4}{26} = \frac{5}{26}$

2. (a)

y	1	2	3	4	5
$P(Y = y)$	$\frac{5}{35}$	$\frac{8}{35}$	$\frac{9}{35}$	$\frac{8}{35}$	$\frac{5}{35}$

   (b) $P(Y \geqslant 3) = \frac{9}{35} + \frac{8}{35} + \frac{5}{35} = \frac{22}{35}$ (or $1 - (\frac{5}{35} + \frac{8}{35}) = \frac{22}{35}$)

3. (a) $a = 0.2$

w	-4	-1	0	1	3	6
$P(W = w)$	0.15	0.4	0.2	0.05	0.1	0.1

   (b) $P(2W + 5 \geqslant 4) = 0.45$

105 Cumulative distribution

1. (a) $F(4) = 1$ that is, $\frac{16 + k}{30} = 1$ so $16 + k = 30$, $k = 14$

   (b) $P(X = 1) = F(1) = \frac{1 + k}{30} = \frac{15}{30}$

   $P(X = 2) = F(2) - F(1)$ and $F(2) = \frac{4 + 14}{30} = \frac{18}{30}$

   so $P(X = 2) = \frac{3}{30}$

   $P(X = 3) = F(3) - F(2)$ and $F(3) = \frac{9 + 14}{30} = \frac{23}{30}$

   so $P(X = 3) = \frac{5}{30}$

   Hence $P(X = 4) = \frac{7}{30}$ since total probability $= 1$

x	1	2	3	4
$P(X = x)$	$\frac{15}{30}$	$\frac{3}{30}$	$\frac{5}{30}$	$\frac{7}{30}$

2. (a) $F(3) = \frac{(6 + k)^2}{81} = 1$ hence $(6 + k)^2 = 81$

   $k^2 + 12k + 36 = 81 \Rightarrow k^2 + 12k - 45 = 0$

   $(k + 15)(k - 3) = 0 \Rightarrow k = -15$ or 3

   $k = 3$ since k cannot be negative

   (b) $F(1) = \frac{25}{81}$ and $F(2) = \frac{49}{81}$

y	1	2	3
$P(Y = y)$	$\frac{25}{81}$	$\frac{24}{81}$	$\frac{32}{81}$

3. (a) $a = 0.3$ $b = 0.4$ $c = 0.1$ $d = 0.6$ $e = 1$

   (b) $P(3W + 2 \leqslant 11) = P(W \leqslant 3) = 0.6$

106 Expectation and variance

1. (a) $E(X) = 1 \times 0.3 + 2 \times 0.05 + 3 \times 0.2 + 4 \times 0.35 + 5 \times 0.1$

   $= 0.3 + 0.1 + 0.6 + 1.4 + 0.5 = 2.9$

   (b) $E(X^2) = 1^2 \times 0.3 + 2^2 \times 0.05 + 3^2 \times 0.2 + 4^2 \times 0.35 + 5^2 \times 0.1$

   $= 0.3 + 0.2 + 1.8 + 5.6 + 2.5 = 10.4$

   $Var(X) = E(X^2) - [E(X)]^2 = 10.4 - (2.9)^2 = 1.99$

2. (a)

y	1	2	3	4
$P(Y = y)$	$\frac{1}{56}$	$\frac{7}{56}$	$\frac{17}{56}$	$\frac{31}{56}$

   (b) $E(Y) = \frac{190}{56}$

   (c) $Var(Y) = E(Y^2) - [E(Y)]^2$ $E(Y^2) = \frac{678}{56}$

   $Var(Y) = 0.596$ (3 s.f.)

3. (a) $a + b = 0.55$

   $a + 2b = 0.8$

   (b) $a = 0.3$ and $b = 0.25$

   (c) $Var(W) = 1.4475$

107 Functions of random variables

1. (a) $E(2X + 3) = 11$ (b) $Var(2X + 3) = 6$
   (c) $E(5 - 3X) = -7$ (d) $Var(5 - 3X) = 13.5$

G 2. (a) Total probability = 1,
   so $k = 1 - (0.1 + 0.15 + 0.05 + 0.30) = 0.4$
   (b) $E(Y) = (-2 \times 0.1) + (0 \times 0.15) + (2 \times 0.05)$
       $+ (4 \times 0.4) + (6 \times 0.3) = 3.3$
   (c) $E(Y^2) = (-2)^2 \times 0.1 + 0^2 \times 0.15 + 2^2 \times 0.05$
       $+ 4^2 \times 0.4 + 6^2 \times 0.3 = 17.8$
       $Var(Y) = E(Y^2) - [E(Y)]^2 = 17.8 - (3.3)^2 = 6.91$
   (d) $E(5Y - 2) = 5 \times E(Y) - 2 = 5(3.3) - 2 = 14.5$
   (e) $Var(5Y - 2) = 5^2 \times Var(Y) = 25 \times 6.91 = 172.75$

3. (a) $E(W) = 0.45$
   (b) $Var(W) = 3.1475$
   (c) $m = 2$
   (d) $Var(T) = 12.59$

108 Normal distribution 1

1. (a) $P(Z < 0.7) = 0.7580$
   (b) $P(Z < 1.44) = 0.9251$
   (c) $P(Z < 2.75) = 0.9970$

G 2. (a) When $x = 7$, $z = \dfrac{x - \mu}{\sigma} = \dfrac{7 - 5}{4} = 0.5$
       $P(X < 7) = P(Z < 0.5) = 0.6915$
   (b) $P(X < 12.12) = P(Z < 1.78) = 0.9625$
   (c) $P(X < 6.48) = P(Z < 0.37) = 0.6443$

3. (a) P(a man is less than 182 cm tall) = 0.7734
   (b) P(both men are less than 182 cm tall) = 0.598 (3 s.f.)
   (c) P(both men are 182 cm or more in height)
       = 0.0513 (3 s.f.)

109 Normal distribution 2

G 1. (a) When $x = 112$, $z = \dfrac{x - \mu}{\sigma} = \dfrac{112 - 100}{10} = 1.2$
       $P(X > 112) = P(Z > 1.2) = 1 - P(Z < 1.2)$
       $= 1 - 0.8849 = 0.1151$
   (b) When $x = 96$, $z = \dfrac{x - \mu}{\sigma} = \dfrac{96 - 100}{10} = -0.4$
       $P(X < 96) = P(Z < -0.4) = P(Z > 0.4) = 1 - P(Z < 0.4)$
       $= 1 - 0.6554 = 0.3446$
   (c) $P(96 < X < 112) = P(-0.4 < Z < 1.2)$
       $= P(Z < 1.2) - P(Z < -0.4)$
       $= 0.8849 - 0.3446 = 0.5403$

2. (a) P(lifetime of over 1540 hours) = 0.0228
   (b) P(lifetime between 1222 and 1540 hours) = 0.7194
   (c) P(both last between 1222 and 1540 hours)
       = 0.518 (3 s.f.)

110 Finding unknown values

G 1. (a) $P(X < a) = P\left(Z < \dfrac{a - 80}{10}\right) = 0.305$
       $1 - 0.305 = 0.695$ and $P(Z < 0.51) = 0.695$
       So $P(Z < -0.51) = 0.305$
       $\dfrac{a - 80}{10} = -0.51$, giving $a = 74.9$

Area = 0.305
$-0.51 \quad 0 \quad 0.51$ z

(b) $P(X > b) = 0.102$
   $P\left(Z > \dfrac{b - 80}{10}\right) = 0.102$
   $P(Z < 1.27) = 0.898$, so $P(Z > 1.27) = 1 - 0.898 = 0.102$
   $\dfrac{b - 80}{10} = 1.27$, giving $b = 92.7$

2. (a) 19 072 miles
   (b) 16 928 miles

3. The middle 70% of the girls are between 156.8 cm and 169.2 cm tall.

111 Finding μ and σ

G 1. $P(X > 440) = P\left(Z > \dfrac{450 - 452}{\sigma}\right) = 0.99$
   $P(Z > -2.3263) = 0.99$ (using the percentage points table)
   since $P(Z > 2.3263) = 0.01$
   $\dfrac{450 - 452}{\sigma} = -2.3263$ giving $\sigma = \dfrac{-12}{-2.3263} = 5.16$ (3 s.f.)

2. (a) $P(X > 20.6) = P\left(Z > \dfrac{20.6 - \mu}{\sigma}\right) = 0.4$
       $P(Z > 0.2533) = 0.4$ (using the percentage points table)
       $\dfrac{20.6 - \mu}{\sigma} = 0.2533 \rightarrow 20.6 - \mu = 0.2533\sigma$
       $\mu = 20.6 - 0.2533\sigma$
   (b) Similarly, $P(Z > 1.0364) = 0.15$ (using the percentage points table)
       $P(Z < -1.0364) = 0.15$, hence $\dfrac{13.2 - \mu}{\sigma} = -1.0364$
       $\mu = 13.2 + 1.0364\sigma$
       Solving simultaneously gives
       $\mu = 19.1$ (3 s.f.) and $\sigma = 5.74$ (3 s.f.)

112–113 You are the examiner!

1. (a) $F(4) = 1$, that is $\dfrac{16 + k}{36} = 1$, so $k = 20$

x	2	3	4
$P(X = x)$	$\frac{24}{36}$	$\frac{5}{36}$	$\frac{7}{36}$

   (b) $P(2) = F(2) = \dfrac{4 + 20}{36} = \dfrac{24}{36}$
       $P(3) = F(3) - P(2) = \dfrac{9 + 20}{36} - \dfrac{24}{36} = \dfrac{5}{36}$
       $P(4) = 1 - F(3) = \dfrac{7}{36}$
   (c) $E(3X + 5) = 3E(X) = \dfrac{3 \times 91}{36} + 5 = \dfrac{273 + 180}{36} = \dfrac{151}{12}$
   (d) $Var(3X + 5) = 3^2 \times Var(X) = \dfrac{9 \times 827}{1296} = \dfrac{827}{144}$

2. (a) Width = 4 cm and height = 4.8 cm
   (b) Median = $119.5 + \dfrac{9 \times 40}{48} = 127$ g

3. (a) Regression line equation is $x = a + bt$
       where $b = \dfrac{S_{tx}}{S_{tt}} = \dfrac{516}{462} = 1.116\,88...$ and
       $a = \bar{x} - b\bar{t} = 15 - (1.116\,88...) \times 16 = -2.8701...$
       so $b = 1.12$ (3 s.f.) and $a = -2.87$ (3 s.f.) and the
       equation is $x = -2.87 + 1.12t$
   (b) When $t = 20$, $x = 19.53$ and $p = 100x + 2500 = 4453$

Decision mathematics 1

114 Flow charts

G 1. (a)

A	B	C	D	Output
6	10	0	0	
		6	10	
		12	20	
		18	20	
		24	30	
		30		30

(b) It works out the lowest common multiple of A and B.

(c) A

2. (a)

A	B	C	N	X	Y	Output
1	-10	24	0	1	15	
				2	8	
				3	3	
			1	4	0	4
				5	-1	
			2	6	0	6

(b) It solves a quadratic equation when the solutions are positive integers.

(c) It checks whether two solutions have been found, to prevent any further calculations.

115 Bubble sort

G 1. (a)

	11	4	9	12	10	
	11	9	4	12	10	(swap 4 and 9)
	11	9	12	4	10	(swap 4 and 12)
1st pass	11	9	12	10	4	(swap 4 and 10 ...) end of first pass
2nd pass	11	12	10	9	4	
3rd pass	12	11	10	9	4	the list is sorted

(b) 3 passes

2.

	D	B	F	E	G	B	
1st pass	B	D	E	F	B	G	
2nd pass	B	D	E	B	F	G	
3rd pass	B	D	B	E	F	G	
4th pass	B	B	D	E	F	G	the list is sorted

3.

	79	26	45	50	81	32	45	63	
1st pass	79	45	50	81	32	45	63	26	
2nd pass	79	50	81	45	45	63	32	26	
3rd pass	79	81	50	45	63	45	32	26	
4th pass	81	79	50	63	45	45	32	26	
5th pass	81	79	63	50	45	45	32	26	the list is sorted

116 Quick sort

G 1.

2.

3.

117 Binary search

G 1.

(C) Chile found

2.

(T) Tottenham Hotspur found

3. (a)

(b)

1215 1492 1492 found

118 Bin packing 1

G 1. (a) $50 + 85 + 68 + 44 + 36 + 60 + 27 = 370$

$370 \div 100 = 3.7$, so 4 crates is the lower bound.

(b)
Crate 1	50	44
Crate 2	85	
Crate 3	68	27
Crate 4	36	60

2. (a) Total = 1071

$1071 \div 300 = 3.57$, so 4 bins is the lower bound.

(b)
Bin 1	175	80		(255)
Bin 2	206	64		(270)
Bin 3	142	125		(267)
Bin 4	97	112	70	(279)

3. (a) Total = $7.6 \div 1.6 = 4.75$, so 5 trolleys is the lower bound.

(b)
Trolley 1	0.9	0.6	(1.5)
Trolley 2	1.2	0.3	(1.5)
Trolley 3	1.3		
Trolley 4	0.8		
Trolley 5	1.4		
Trolley 6	1.1		

(c) The wasted space (2 m) is more than the height of one trolley. It is not an optimal solution because an optimal solution would be 5 trolleys and here 6 are needed.

119 Bin packing 2

G 1. (a)
Bin 1	60	18		(78)
Bin 2	58	13		(71)
Bin 3	47	29		(76)
Bin 4	42	25	12	(79)
Bin 5	10			

(b) Lower bound = 314 ÷ 80 = 3.925, so 4 bins is the lower bound.

Full bin 1 58   12   10   (80)
Full bin 2 42   25   13   (80)
Bin 3   60   18   (78)
Bin 4   47   29   (76)

This solution is optimal because it matches the lower bound.
There is very little (only 6 kg) wasted space.

2. (a) Shelf 1   2.7
Shelf 2   2.5
Shelf 3   1.5   1.2   (2.7)
Shelf 4   1.0   0.9   0.8   (2.7)
Shelf 5   0.6
Empty shelf space = 0.3 + 0.5 + 0.3 + 0.3 + 2.4 = 3.8 m

(b) Full shelf 1 1.5   0.9   0.6
Full shelf 2 1.2   1.0   0.8
Shelf 3   2.7   (0.3)
Shelf 4   2.5   (0.5)
Empty shelf space = 0.3 + 0.5 = 0.8 m
Optimal solution since lower bound = 11.2 ÷ 3 = 3.73...,
so 4 shelves needed, as in this solution.

120 Graphs

1. (a)

Vertex	A	B	C	D	E	F
Degree	3	2	1	4	4	2

(b) e.g.

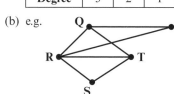

2. (a) (i) Yes, e.g. **PRVQ**
     (ii) Yes, e.g. **RSTU**
(b) **QVT** and **QVRST**

3. (a) 4
(b) (i) **CAEF** or **CBAEF** or **CADF**
     (ii) **ABCA**
(c) (i) **ADEF**; no, there is no route from **D** to **E**
     (ii) **FDACB**; yes
     (iii) **EACBAD**; no, because **A** is repeated
(d) (i)

or

     (ii)

121 Drawing networks

1. (a)

	A	B	C	D	E
A	–	3	–	–	–
B	3	–	4	–	6
C	–	4	–	5	10
D	–	–	5	–	8
E	–	6	10	8	–

(b)

	P	Q	R	S	T
P	–	11	18	12	10
Q	11	–	9	–	13
R	18	9	–	4	–
S	12	–	4	–	3
T	10	13	–	3	–

2.

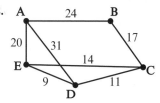

3. (a)

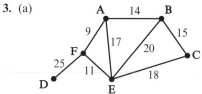

(b) e.g.

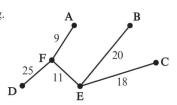

(c) e.g. 83 (for the spanning tree diagram in part (b))

122 Kruskal's algorithm

1. (a) and (b)

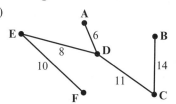

AD (6) ✓ **DE** (8) ✓ **AE** (9) ✗ **EF** (10) ✓ **DC** (11) ✓
DF (13) ✗ **BC** (14) ✓ **BF** (15) ✗ **AB** (18) ✗

(c) Weight of minimum spanning tree = 49

2. (a)

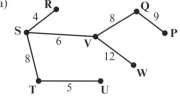

RS (4) ✓ **TU** (5) ✓ **SV** (6) ✓ **RV** (7) ✗ **VQ** (8) ✓
ST (8) ✓ **QP** (9) ✓ **RQ** (10) ✗ **VU** (10) ✗
VP (11) ✗ **VW** (12) ✓ **WP** (14) ✗

(b) Weight of minimum connector = 52

3. (a)

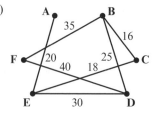

(b) **BC** (16) ✓ **CE** (18) ✓ **AE** (20) ✓ **BD** (25) ✓
DE (30) ✗ **BF** (35) ✓ **DF** (40) ✗

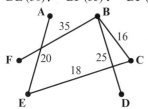

(c) Weight of minimum spanning tree = 114

123 Prim's algorithm

G 1. (a)

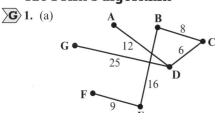

DC (6) **CB** (8) **DA** (12) **BE** (16) **EF** (9) **DG** (25)

(b) Weight of minimum spanning tree = 76

G 2.

	1	3		4	2
	P	**Q**	**R**	**S**	**T**
P	–	25	–	30	12
Q	25	–	35	24	(20)
R	–	35	–	(18)	40
S	30	(24)	18	–	32
T	(12)	20	40	32	–

PT (12) **TQ** (20) **QS** (24) **SR** (18)

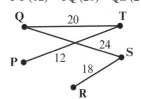

3.

	1	3		2	5	6	4
	H	**I**	**J**	**K**	**L**	**M**	**N**
H	–	25	–	15	–	20	–
I	25	–	18	(13)	–	–	–
J	–	(18)	–	–	28	–	22
K	(15)	13	–	–	–	–	14
L	–	–	28	–	–	9	(11)
M	20	–	–	(9)	–	–	12
N	–	–	22	(14)	11	12	–

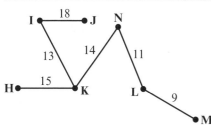

HK (15) **KI** (13) **KN** (14) **NL** (11) **LM** (9) **IJ** (18)
Total length is 80 km

124 Dijkstra's algorithm

G 1.

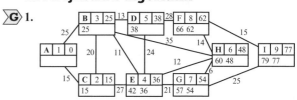

Shortest route is **ABEHFI**, and time taken is 77 minutes.

2. (a)

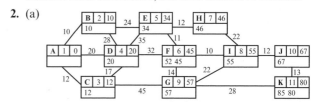

Harry's route is **ABEFIJK**, 80 km, taking 2 hours.

(b) If **J** to **K** is blocked, the shortest route is **ACGK**, 85 km,
taking $85 \div 40 = 2.125$ hours
0.125 hours $= \frac{1}{8}$ of an hour = 7.5 minutes longer than
before.

125 Route inspection

G 1. Degree of vertices: **A** 2 **B** 3 **C** 2 **D** 5 **E** 3 **F** 2 **G** 3 **H** 2
Odd vertices: **B, D, E, G**
Possible pairings: **BD** + **EG** (through **D**) = 16 + 18 = 34
  BE (through **C**) + **DG** = 20 + 12 = 32
  BG (through **D**) + **DE** = 28 + 6 = 34
Link vertices **B** and **E** by repeating arcs **BC** and **CE**.
Link vertices **D** and **G** by repeating arc **DG**.
Length of route = 139 km + 32 km = 171 km

2. (a) Degree of vertices: **A** 4 **B** 3 **C** 3 **D** 4 **E** 3 **F** 4 **G** 3
Odd vertices: **B, C, E, G**

(b) Possible pairings:
BC + **EG** (through **F**) = 13 + 14 = 27
BE (through **A**) + **CG** = 16 + 7 = 23
BG + **CE** (through **D**) = 8 + 18 = 26
Link vertices **B** and **E** by repeating arcs **BA** and **AE**.
Link vertices **C** and **G** by repeating arc **CG**.

(c) Length of route = 102 + 23 = 125
Inspection route e.g. **D, A, B, A, E, A, F, E, D, F, G, B, C, G, C, D**

126 Activity networks

G 1. (a) A dotted line is a dummy activity.
The one from event 2 to event 4 shows that activity **E**
depends on activity **A** as well as on activity **B**.
The one from event 3 to event 4 shows that activity **E**
also depends on activity **C**, so activity **E** depends on all
three activities **A, B** and **C**.

(b)

Activity	Preceded by
A	–
B	–
C	–
D	A
E	A, B, C
F	C
G	D
H	E, F, G

2.

Activity	Preceded by
A	–
B	–
C	A, B
D	A, B
E	B
F	E
G	C, D, F

G 3.

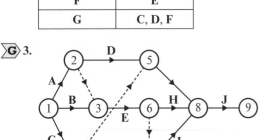

127 Early and late times

G 1.

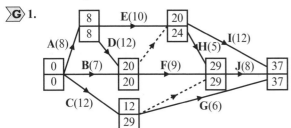

2.

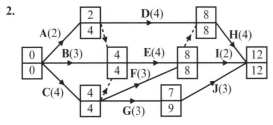

3.

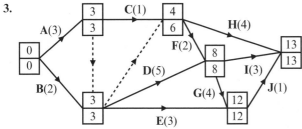

128 Critical paths

G 1. (a)

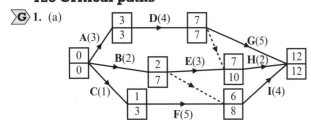

(b) Critical path is **A, D, G**

(c) For **F**, total float = 8 − 1 − 5 = 2
For **E**, total float = 10 − 2 − 3 = 5
For **H**, total float = 12 − 7 − 2 = 3

Activity	E	F	H
Total float	5	2	3

2. (a)

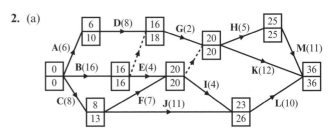

(b) Critical path is **B, E, H, M**

(c)

Activity	A	F	J
Total float	4	5	7

(d) Activity **A** can start any time in the first 4 minutes without delaying the whole process.

129 Gantt charts

G 1. (a) Critical path is **A, F, H, J**

(b) For **B**, total float = 12 − 0 − 8 = 4

Activity	B	C	D	E	G	I
Total float	4	1	2	1	1	2

(c)

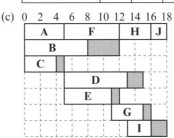

2. (a) Critical path is **B, F, H, J, L**

(b)

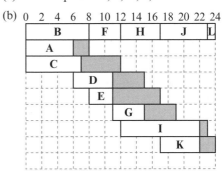

130 Scheduling

G 1. (a) Lower bound = 60 ÷ 26 = 2.307... which rounds up to 3 workers.

(b) e.g.

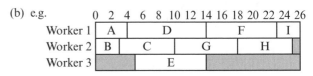

2. (a) **D** and **F**

(b) Lower bound = 84 ÷ 36 = 2.33... which rounds up to 3 workers.

(c) e.g.

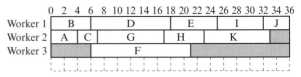

131 Linear programming 1

 1. Let x = number of bags of Happycat
Let y = number of bags of Moggie
$x \geqslant 0$ and $y \geqslant 0$
Cost = $5x + 3y$ so $5x + 3y \leqslant 120$
Total bags = $x + y$ so $x + y \geqslant 30$
x must be at least half of y so $x \geqslant \dfrac{y}{2}$
Profit = $8x + 6y$ to be maximised.

2. Let x = number of tables
Let y = number of chairs
$x \geqslant 0$ and $y \geqslant 0$
Production time = $6x + 5y$ so $6x + 5y \leqslant 120$
Assembly time = $3x + y$ so $3x + y \leqslant 36$
Profit = $140x + 80y$ to be maximised.

3. Let x = number of tablets
Let y = number of doses of liquid
$x \geqslant 0$ and $y \geqslant 0$
Number of units of antibiotic = $2x + 3y$ so $2x + 3y \geqslant 18$
Number of units of vitamin = $4x + 3y$ so $4x + 3y \geqslant 24$
Number of units of nutrient = $5x + 20y$ so $5x + 20y \geqslant 80$
Cost = $0.9x + 2.4y$ to be minimised.

132 Linear programming 2

 1. $5x + 4y = 200$: when $x = 0$, $y = 50$ and when $y = 0$, $x = 40$
$2x + 5y = 100$: when $x = 0$, $y = 20$ and when $y = 0$, $x = 50$
$y = 2x$: plot $(0, 0)$ and $(20, 40)$

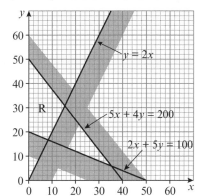

2.

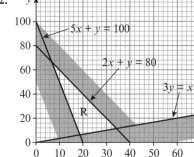

3. (a) $y \leqslant x + 20$ and $y \geqslant \dfrac{x}{2}$

(b)

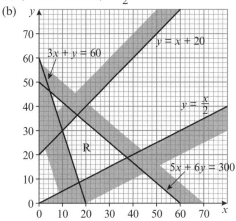

133 Objective lines

1. (a) $3x + 2y = 30$: $(10, 0)$ and $(0, 15)$ lie on this line (the objective line).
U and V as shown on graph below.

(b) $U = (0, 20)$, minimum $P = 40$
$V = (5, 30)$, maximum $P = 75$

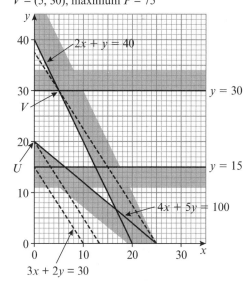

2. (a) $x + 2y = 20$: points $(20, 0)$ and $(0, 10)$ lie on this line.
U and V as shown on graph below.

(b) For minimum, $U = (35, 10)$ and $P = 55$
For maximum, $V = (60, 16)$ and $P = 92$

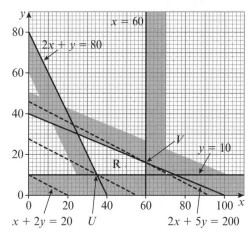

134 Vertex testing

1. Solving simultaneously: $3x + y = 9$ ①
$2x - y = 4$ ②
$5x = 13$, so $x = 2.6$

Substitute into ①: $3(2.6) + y = 9$, so $y = 1.2$ (call this A)
From the graph, the other points of intersection are:
$B = (1, 6)$, $C = (4, 6)$ and $D = (4, 4)$
A: $x = 2.6$ $y = 1.2$ $P = 4x + 3y = 10.4 + 3.6 = 14$
B: $x = 1$ $y = 6$ $P = 4x + 3y = 4 + 18 = 22$
C: $x = 4$ $y = 6$ $P = 4x + 3y = 16 + 18 = 34$
D: $x = 4$ $y = 4$ $P = 4x + 3y = 16 + 12 = 28$
Minimum P is 14 when $x = 2.6$ and $y = 1.2$

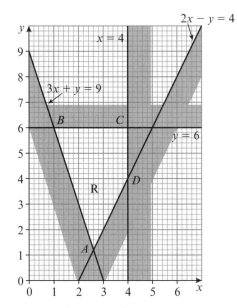

2x − y = 4

x = 4

3x + y = 9

B   C

y = 6

R

D

A

2. (a)
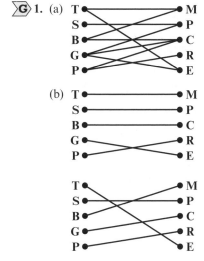

4x − y = 7

x = 1

A   B

y = 13

R

D

C

5x + 3y = 30

(b) Points of intersection are:
$A = (1, 13)$, $B = (5, 13)$, $C = (3, 5)$, $D = (1, 8\frac{1}{3})$
A: $x = 1$ $y = 13$ $P = 6y − 7x = 78 − 7 = 71$
B: $x = 5$ $y = 13$ $P = 6y − 7x = 78 − 35 = 43$
C: $x = 3$ $y = 5$ $P = 6y − 7x = 30 − 21 = 9$
D: $x = 1$ $y = 8\frac{1}{3}$ $P = 6y − 7x = 50 − 7 = 43$
Minimum P is 9 when $x = 3$ and $y = 5$
Maximum P is 71 when $x = 1$ and $y = 13$

135 Matchings on graphs

G 1. (a)
T — M
S — P
B — C
G — R
P — E

(b)
T — M
S — P
B — C
G — R
P — E

T — M
S — P
B — C
G — R
P — E

2. These are the two possible solutions.

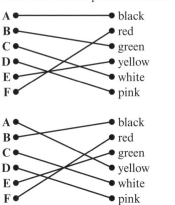
A — black
B — red
C — green
D — yellow
E — white
F — pink

A — black
B — red
C — green
D — yellow
E — white
F — pink

136 Maximum matchings

G 1. (a) Alternating path: $A − 5 = D − 4 = F − 2$
Change status: $A = 5 − D = 4 − F = 2$
New matching: $A = 5, B = 1, D = 4, E = 3, F = 2$

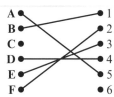
A — 1
B — 2
C   3
D — 4
E — 5
F   6

(b) Alternating path: $C − 3 = E − 6$
Change status: $C = 3 − E = 6$
New matching: $A = 5, B = 1, C = 3$
$D = 4, E = 6, F = 2$

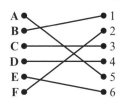
A — 1
B — 2
C — 3
D — 4
E — 5
F   6

2. (a) e.g. Alternating path: $K − 2 = G − 3 = I − 5 = H − 1$
Change status: $K = 2 − G = 3 − I = 5 − H = 1$
New matching: $G = 3, H = 1, I = 5, K = 2, L = 4$

G   1
H   2
I   3
J   4
K   5
L   6

(b) Alternating path: $J − 4 = L − 6$
Change status: $J = 4 − L = 6$ now complete
$G = 3, H = 1, I = 5, J = 4, K = 2, L = 6$

G   1
H   2
I   3
J   4
K   5
L — 6

137 Which algorithm?

1. Putting a list into alphabetical or numerical order, writing a full list after each pass.

Finding a minimum spanning tree for a network, listing the arcs included or rejected in the correct order.

Putting a list into alphabetical or numerical order, showing all pivots.

Working out the shortest route to travel along all arcs in a network.

Finding a minimum spanning tree for a network by selecting a vertex and adding the arc of least weight that joins a new vertex to the tree.

Putting items listed in descending order into equal sized compartments, stating which items go in which compartment and in which order

Prim's algorithm

First-fit decreasing bin-packing

Route inspection

Kruskal's algorithm

Quick sort

Bubble sort

138–139 You are the examiner!

1. (a) R D C L T Ⓝ H S A E

D C L Ⓗ A E Ⓝ R Ⓣ S

D C Ⓐ E Ⓗ Ⓛ Ⓝ R Ⓢ Ⓣ

Ⓐ D Ⓒ E Ⓗ Ⓛ Ⓝ Ⓡ Ⓢ Ⓣ

Ⓐ Ⓒ D Ⓔ Ⓗ Ⓛ Ⓝ Ⓡ Ⓢ Ⓣ

Ⓐ Ⓒ Ⓓ Ⓔ Ⓗ Ⓛ Ⓝ Ⓡ Ⓢ Ⓣ

(b) A C D E H Ⓛ ~~N R S T~~

~~A C~~ Ⓓ E H

~~E~~ Ⓗ

Ⓔ Exe has been found.

2. (a) Kruskal: order of arcs:
CE (8) ✓   **BF** (10) ✓   **CD** (10) ✓   **EG** (12) ✓
CH (14) ✓   **AB** (15) ✓   **EH** (16) ✗   **AG** (17) ✓
BE (18) ✗   **AF** (20) ✗   **BC** (24) ✗

(b) Prim: starting at **E**, order of arcs:
CE (8), **CD** (10), **EG** (12), **CH** (14), **AG** (17), **AB** (15), **BF** (10)

(c) Minimum spanning tree: weight = 86

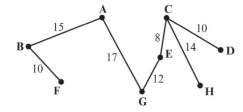

3. (a) Let x be the number of headphones and y be the number of speakers
Maximise Profit = $30x + 20y$ subject to these constraints:
$x > y$, $y \geqslant 5$, $x + y \geqslant 20$
$12x + 16y \leqslant 672$ (upper limit on headphones)
$5x + 17y \leqslant 425$ (upper limit on speakers)

(b)

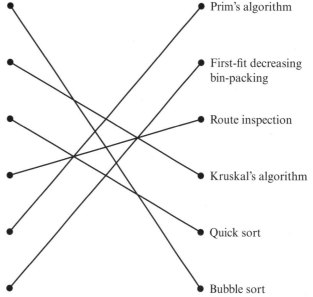

$30x + 20y = 300$ (or $3x + 2y = 30$)

C1 Practice paper

1. $y = 12x + 8$
2. $\sqrt{5} - \sqrt{3}$
3. $\dfrac{x^4}{2} - 5x - \dfrac{3}{x} + c$
4. C: $y = 2x(x - 1) = 2x^2 - 2x$
   L: $2y = 5x - 10$
   Points of intersection given by $2(2x^2 - 2x) = 5x - 10$,
   so $4x^2 - 9x + 10 = 0$
   $b^2 - 4ac = 81 - 4 \times 4 \times 10 = 81 - 160 < 0$
   Therefore no points of intersection.
5. (a) $x > 3$
   (b) $x < -8$ and $x > 2$
6. $y = x^3 - 7x^2 + 8x + 11$
7. (a) $a_2 = 15 + c$
   (b) $a_3 = 3a_2 + c = 3(15 + c) + c = 45 + 4c$
   (c) $c < 3$
8. (a) $S_5 = \dfrac{5}{2}[2M + 4(2H)] = 5M + 20H$
   (b) $H = 600$
   (c) $M = 17\,600$
9. (a) $k = -2$
   (b) $-\dfrac{2}{5}$
   (c) $5x - 2y + 24 = 0$
   (d) $(0, 12)$
   (e) $2\sqrt{29}$
10. (a) $\dfrac{dy}{dx} = \dfrac{3}{4}x^2 - 6\sqrt{x} + \dfrac{12}{x^2}$
    (b) When $x = 4$:
        $y = \dfrac{1}{4}(4)^3 - 4(4)^{\frac{3}{2}} - \dfrac{12}{4} + 18 = 16 - 32 - 3 + 18 = -1$
        So $(4, -1)$ lies on C.
    (c) $4x + 3y - 13 = 0$
11. (a)

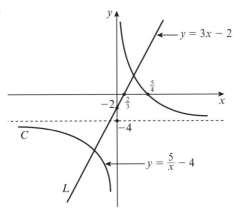

    (b) $x = 0$ (or the y-axis) and $y = -4$
    (c) $(-\dfrac{5}{3}, -7)$ and $(1, 1)$

C2 Practice paper

1. (a)

x	2	2.25	2.5	2.75	3
y	1.2	**0.84**	**0.63**	0.49	0.4

   (b) 0.69
2. (a) $r = \dfrac{2}{3}$
   (b) $a = 405$
   (c) $S_{10} = 1190$ (3 s.f)
   (d) $S_\infty = 1215$
3. (a) $f(-1) = 0$
       so $1 - 1 + a + 3 + b = 0$
       giving $a + b = -3$
   (b) $a = -5, b = 2$

4. (a) $1 + 2x + \dfrac{9}{5}x^2 + \dfrac{24}{25}x^3$
   (b) 1.2190 (4 d.p.)
5. (a) $2\log_5(x - 4) - \log_5(2x - 13) = 1$
       $\log_5(x - 4)^2 - \log_5(2x - 13) = 1$
       $\log_5 \dfrac{(x - 4)^2}{2x - 13} = 1$
       $\dfrac{(x - 4)^2}{2x - 13} = 5$
       $(x - 4)^2 = 10x - 65$
       $x^2 - 8x + 16 = 10x - 65$
       $x^2 - 18x + 81 = 0$
   (b) $x = 9$
6. $(4, -5)$
7. (a) (i) $(12, 6)$
       (ii) 10
   (b) $10\sqrt{5}$
   (c) 20
8. (a) $x = 268.6°, x = 351.4°$
   (b) $x = \dfrac{7\pi}{6}, x = \dfrac{11\pi}{6}$
9. (a) $A = (-4, 2), B = (-1, 5)$
   (b) $\dfrac{9}{2}$

M1 Practice paper

1. (a) Taking $\longrightarrow$ as positive:

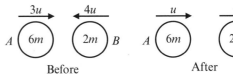

        Before   After

   Conservation of momentum:
   $6m \times 3u + 2m \times (-4u) = 6m \times u + 2m \times v$
   $4mu = 2mv$
   $2u = v$

   B moves with speed $2u$ and its direction is reversed.

   (b) Impulse = change in momentum of A
              = momentum after − momentum before
              = $6m \times u - 6m \times 3u$
              = $-12mu$

   Magnitude of impulse = $12mu$

2.

   Let the reactions at A and B be R.
   (a) Taking moments about C:
       $R \times 12 + R \times 2 = 30g \times 6 + 40g \times 8.8$
       $14R = 180g + 352g$
       $R = \dfrac{532}{14}g = 38g$

   Magnitude of force exerted on beam by support at
   $A = 38g$

   (b) Resolving vertically: $2R = 40g + 30g + Mg$
                            $76g = 70g + Mg$
                            $M = 6$

3. (a)

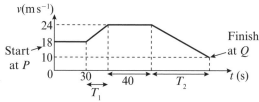

(b) $v = u + at$, so $24 = 18 + 0.3 \times T_1 \Rightarrow T_1 = 20$.
So, time accelerating $= 20\,\text{s}$

(c) Area under graph $= 2855$
$2855 = 18 \times 30 + \frac{1}{2} \times 20 \times (18 + 24) + 24 \times 40 +$
$\qquad \frac{1}{2} \times T_2 \times (24 + 10)$
$2855 = 540 + 420 + 960 + 17 \times T_2$
$2855 = 1920 + 17 \times T_2 \Rightarrow T_2 = 55$
Time taken to move from P to $Q = 30 + 20 + 40 + 55$
$\qquad\qquad\qquad\qquad\qquad\qquad = 145\,\text{s}$

4. Taking ↑ as positive throughout:

(a) $s = 0$, $u = 18.6$, $a = -9.8$, $t = ?$
$s = ut + \frac{1}{2}at^2$
$0 = 18.6t - 4.9t^2$
$0 = t(18.6 - 4.9t)$
$t = 0$ or $t = \dfrac{18.6}{4.9} = 3.8\,\text{s}$
Time for stone to return to $A = 3.8\,\text{s}$
(Could also use $v = u + at$ to find time to greatest height, then double this time.)

(b) $s = ?$, $u = 18.6$, $v = 0$, $a = -9.8$
$v^2 = u^2 + 2as$
$0 = 18.6^2 - 19.6s$
$s = \dfrac{18.6^2}{19.6} = 17.6510... \approx 18\,\text{m}$ (2 s.f.)

(c) $s = 9$, $u = 18.6$, $a = -9.8$, $t = ?$
$s = ut + \frac{1}{2}at^2$
$9 = 18.6t - 4.9t^2$
$4.9t^2 - 18.6t + 9 = 0$
$t = \dfrac{18.6 \pm \sqrt{(18.6^2 - 4(4.9)(9))}}{9.8}$
Leading to $t = 3.22668...$ or $0.56923...$
Stone is at height $9\,\text{m}$ between $0.57\,\text{s}$ and $3.23\,\text{s}$, i.e. for a time of $2.66 \approx 2.7\,\text{s}$ (2 s.f.)

5. (a)

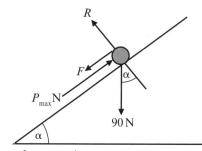

$\mu = \frac{2}{3}$, $\tan\alpha = \frac{4}{3}$
$\sin\alpha = \frac{4}{5}$ and $\cos\alpha = \frac{3}{5}$
If P is maximum then the particle is on the point of moving up the plane, so the frictional force must act down the plane.
Normal reaction, $R = 90\cos\alpha = 90 \times \frac{3}{5} = 54\,\text{N}$
$F_{max} = \mu R = \frac{2}{3} \times 54 = 36\,\text{N}$
Resolving parallel to the plane: $P_{max} = F_{max} + 90\sin\alpha$
$\qquad\qquad\qquad\qquad P_{max} = 36 + 90 \times \frac{4}{5}$
$\qquad\qquad\qquad\qquad P_{max} = 36 + 72 = 108\,\text{N}$

(b)

$P = 40$, so P is not at its maximum value, which means that the particle will have a tendency to slide down the plane, so the frictional force must act up the plane.
Resolving parallel to the plane: $40 + F = 90\sin\alpha$
$\qquad\qquad\qquad\qquad F = 72 - 40 = 32\,\text{N}$

6. (a) (i) $\mathbf{p} = (2\mathbf{i} + 5\mathbf{j}) + t(6\mathbf{i} - 14\mathbf{j}) = (2 + 6t)\mathbf{i} + (5 - 14t)\mathbf{j}$
(ii) $\mathbf{q} = (-2\mathbf{i}) + t(10\mathbf{i} - 12\mathbf{j}) = (-2 + 10t)\mathbf{i} - 12t\mathbf{j}$
(iii) $\overrightarrow{PQ} = \mathbf{q} - \mathbf{p} = (-4 + 4t)\mathbf{i} + (-5 + 2t)\mathbf{j}$

(b) When P is due west of Q, the $\mathbf{j}$ component of $\overrightarrow{PQ}$ must be zero. $-5 + 2t = 0$, so $t = 2.5$ (or 12.30 pm)

(c)

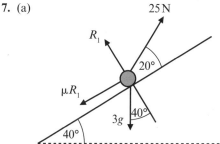

When P is north-west of Q, the $\mathbf{i}$ and $\mathbf{j}$ components of $\overrightarrow{PQ}$ must be equal in value but opposite in sign (as shown in diagram),
i.e. $(-5 + 2t) = -(-4 + 4t) \Rightarrow t = 1.5$
When $t = 1.5$, $\mathbf{p} = 11\mathbf{i} - 16\mathbf{j}$
and $\mathbf{q} = 13\mathbf{i} - 18\mathbf{j}$

7. (a)

Using $F = ma$ perpendicular to the plane,
$R_1 + 25\sin 20° - 3g\cos 40° = 0$
$\Rightarrow R_1 = 13.9712... \approx 14\,\text{N}$ (2 s.f.)

(b) The frictional force takes its limiting value, $F = \mu R_1 = 14\mu$
Using $F = ma$ parallel to the plane, taking up the plane as positive:
$25\cos 20° - 14\mu - 3g\sin 40° = 0$
(constant speed, so $a = 0$)
$14\mu = 25\cos 20° - 3g\sin 40°$
$\Rightarrow \mu = 0.328... \approx 0.33$ (2 s.f.)

(c)

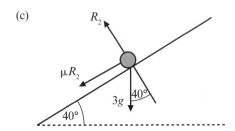

When the 25 N force is removed, there will be a change in the value of the normal reaction.

Using $F = ma$ perpendicular to the plane:

$R_2 - 3g \cos 40° = 0$, $R_2 = 3g \cos 40°$

Force acting down the plane causing the deceleration = $(\mu R_2 + 3g \sin 40°)$

Using $F = ma$ parallel to the plane, taking up the plane as positive:

$-(\mu 3g \cos 40° + 3g \sin 40°) = 3a \Rightarrow a = -8.7629...$

$s = ?$ $u = 13$ $v = 0$ $a = -8.7629...$

$v^2 = u^2 + 2as$

$0 = 13^2 - 2 \times (-8.7629...) \times s$

$\Rightarrow s = 9.6428... \approx 9.6$ m (2 s.f.), the distance that P travels before it comes to rest.

S1 Practice paper

1. (a) Median = 50.4 min
   (b) Mean = 55.7 min
      Standard deviation = 29.8 min

2. (a)

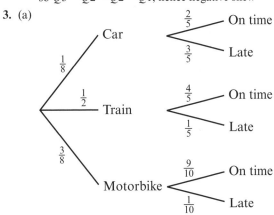

Only one of these whiskers to be drawn

Test score

   (b) $Q3 - Q2 = 4$ and $Q2 - Q1 = 12$
      so $Q3 - Q2 < Q2 - Q1$, hence negative skew

3. (a)

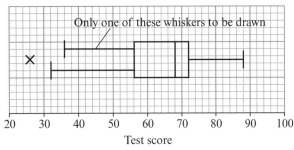

   (b) P(Late) = $\frac{17}{80}$
   (c) P(Car | Late) = $\frac{6}{17}$

4. (a) $F(4) = \dfrac{16 + k}{25} = 1$, so $16 + k = 25$, hence $k = 9$
   (b)

x	-1	2	3	4
$P(X = x)$	$\frac{10}{25}$	$\frac{3}{25}$	$\frac{5}{25}$	$\frac{7}{25}$

   (c) $E(X) = \frac{39}{25}$
   (d) $E(X^2) = \frac{179}{25}$
   (e) $Var(4 - 5X) = \frac{2954}{25}$

5. (a) $S_{xx} = 229.875$ $S_{xy} = -139.875$
   (b) $r = -0.962$ (3 s.f.)
   (c) $y = 26.6 - 0.608x$
   (d) 22 mpg

6. (a) Medium = 27.43%
      Extra large = 11.51%
      Large = 61.06%
   (b) P(Both large) = 0.3728...
   (c) $\mu = 77.8$ and $\sigma = 4.14$ (both to 3 s.f.)

7. (a) $P(A \cap B) = 0.16$
   (b) $P(A' \cap B) = 0.32$
   (c) $P(A' \mid B) = \frac{2}{3}$
   (d) $P(A \cap C) = 0.06$
   (e)

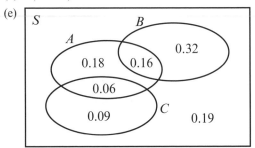

   (f) $P(A \cup C') = 0.91$

D1 Practice paper

1.

30	45	85	15	40	50	20	
45	85	30	40	50	20	15	end of 1st pass
85	45	40	50	30	20	15	end of 2nd pass
85	45	50	40	30	20	15	end of 3rd pass
85	50	45	40	30	20	15	end of 4th pass, list is sorted.

2. Using Diagram 1 provided for Q2.

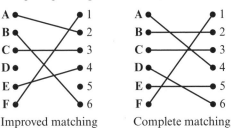

   Improved matching   Complete matching

   (a) Alternating path $C - 3 = B - 6 = E - 4 = A - 2$
      Change status $C = 3 - B = 6 - E = 4 - A = 2$
      New matching $C = 3, B = 6, E = 4, A = 2, F = 1$
   (b) Task 5 cannot be matched to anyone (until **E** learns to do it).
   (c) **B** can now match with 2 (as well as 3 and 6) and **E** can now match with 5 (as well as 4 and 6).
      Alternating path $D - 6 = B - 2 = A - 4 = E - 5$
      Change status $D = 6 - B = 2 - A = 4 - E = 5$
      Complete matching $D = 6, B = 2, A = 4, E = 5, C = 3,$
                          $F = 1$

There are two other possible solutions:

1 For improved matching

   Alternating path $D - 3 = B - 6 = E - 4 = A - 2$

   Change status $D = 3 - B = 6 - E = 4 - A = 2$

   New matching $D = 3, B = 6, E = 4, A = 2, F = 1$

   For complete matching

   Alternating path $C - 3 = D - 6 = B - 2 = A - 4$
   $= E - 5$

   Change status $C = 3 - D = 6 - B = 2 - A = 4 - E = 5$

   Complete matching as in first solution.

2 For improved matching

   Alternating path $D - 6 = E - 4 = A - 2$

   Change status $D = 6 - E = 4 - A = 2$

   New matching $D = 6, B = 3, E = 4, A = 2, F = 1$

   For complete matching

   Alternating path $C - 3 = B - 2 = A - 4 = E - 5$

   Change status $C = 3 - B = 2 - A = 4 - E = 5$

   Complete matching as in first solution.

3. 20   12   19   15   13   21   18

(a) Lower bound = sum of weights ÷ maximum capacity
   = 118 ÷ 30 = 3.9333... which rounds up
   to 4 crates

(b) Crate 1   20
   Crate 2   12   15
   Crate 3   19
   Crate 4   13
   Crate 5   21
   Crate 6   18

(c) Crate 1 (full crate)   18   12
   Crate 2   20
   Crate 3   19
   Crate 4   15   13
   Crate 5   21

(d) There are five weights of 15 kg or more. No two of
   these can be paired, so five crates will be needed.

4. (a) Using Diagram 2 provided for Q4.

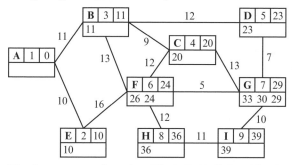

The shortest route from **A** to **I** is **A, B, F, G, I** and is of
length 39 miles.

(b) If **FG** is closed, the new shortest route will be **A, B, D,
   G, I** of length 40 miles. (**B** to **G** via **F** is 18 miles, **B** to **G**
   via **D** is 19 miles)

5. (a) (i) A tree is a connected graph with no cycles.

   (ii) A minimum spanning tree is a tree containing all
      vertices, with the smallest possible length.

(b) Using Kruskal's algorithm:

   WB (40) ✓   WE (50) ✓   AF (55) ✓   FE (60) ✓
   FW (60) ✗   BC (60) ✓   ED (65) ✓   AW (70) ✗
   CD (70) ✗   WD (75) ✗   BD (80) ✗   AB (85) ✗
   WC (90) ✗

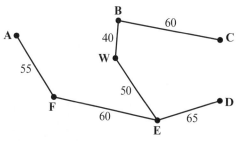

Minimum length = 330 m. **FW** could replace **FE** (they
might have been listed in the opposite order.)

(c) Using Prim's algorithm :

   AF (55) **FE** (60) **WE** (50) **WB** (40) **BC** (60) **ED** (65)

   Minimum spanning tree with **FW** used instead of **FE** is:

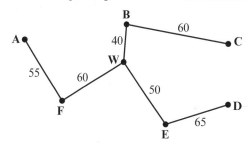

Using Prim's algorithm :

   AF (55) **FW** (60) **WB** (40) **WE** (50) **BC** (60) **ED** (65)

(d) See trees above. **FW** can be used instead of **FE**. Both
   are length 60 so we can choose either once **AF** has been
   selected as the first arc. So the minimum spanning tree
   is not unique.

6. This is the network of roads:

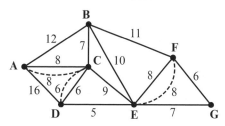

The total weight of the network is 105 km

(a)

Vertex	A	B	C	D	E	F	G
Degree	3	4	4	3	5	3	2

Four odd vertices: **A, D, E** and **F**

Possible pairings:

   AD + **EF** = 14 + 8 = 22 (minimum pairing)
   AE + **DF** = 17 + 13 = 30
   AF + **DE** = 23 + 5 = 28

Repeat arcs **AC, CD** and **EF** to give a minimum route
of 105 + 22 = 127 km.

186

(b) New road **AE** = 14 means a change in the degrees of **A** (now 4) and **E** (now 6).

The weight of the network with the new road is 105 + 14 = 119

Now only two odd vertices, **D** and **F**, so the arcs from **D** to **F** are repeated i.e. **DE** + **EF** = 5 + 8 = 13

Hence new minimum route will be of length 119 + 13 = 132 km, an increase of 5 km.

7. (a) $y \leqslant 3x$ (from line 1) and $y \geqslant \frac{4}{5}x$ (from line 2)

(b) $x + 4y \geqslant 80$ (shown by line 3) and $4x + 5y \leqslant 400$ (shown by line 4)

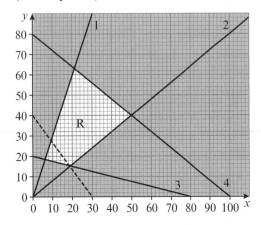

(c) To maximise $P = 4x + 3y$, let $4x + 3y = 120$ so that (30, 0) and (0, 40) lie on the objective line.

Move parallel to this line. The maximum value of P is found when the line leaves the feasible region.

Maximum value is when $x = 50$ and $y = 40$, so $P_{max} = 4(50) + 3(40) = 320$

8. (a) (i) The dummy from event 2 to event 3 is necessary because activities **C** and **D** both depend on activities **A** and **B**.

(ii) The dummy from event 10 to event 11 is necessary because no two activities, **J** and **K** in this case, can share both the same start event number and the same finish event number.

(b) Using Diagram 3 provided for Q8 (b).

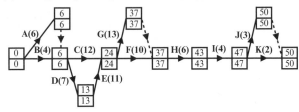

(c) The critical activities are: **A, D, E, G, H, I, J**

(d) Activity **F** has latest finish time 37, earliest start time 24 and its duration is 10 so, total float on activity **F** = 37 − 24 − 10 = 3

(e) Float for other non-critical activities:

B = 6 − 0 − 4 = 2   **C** = 24 − 6 − 12 = 6
K = 50 − 47 − 2 = 1

Using Diagram 3 provided for Q8 (e).

Published by Pearson Education Limited, Edinburgh Gate, Harlow, Essex, CM20 2JE.

www.pearsonschoolsandfecolleges.co.uk

Copies of official specifications for all Edexcel qualifications may be found on the Edexcel website: www.edexcel.com

Text © Pearson Education Limited 2014
Edited by Project One Publishing Solutions, Scotland
Typeset and illustrated by Tech-Set Ltd, Gateshead
Original illustrations © Pearson Education Limited 2014
Cover illustration by Miriam Sturdee

The rights of Su Nicholson and Glyn Payne to be identified as authors of this work have been asserted by them in accordance with the Copyright, Designs and Patents Act 1988.

First published 2014

18 17 16 15 14
10 9 8 7 6 5 4 3 2 1

British Library Cataloguing in Publication Data
A catalogue record for this book is available from the British Library

ISBN 978 1 447 96168 0

Printed in Slovakia by Neografia

Acknowledgements
The following Edexcel examination questions are reproduced with permission from Edexcel:
Question 1 on page 59 © Edexcel 2009; Question 1 on page 60 © Edexcel 2007;
Question 1 on page 64 © Edexcel 2013; Question 1 on page 69 © Edexcel 2009.

Every effort has been made to trace the copyright holders and we apologise in advance for any unintentional omissions. We would be pleased to insert the appropriate acknowledgement in any subsequent edition of this publication.

In the writing of this book, no Edexcel examiners authored sections relevant to examination papers for which they have responsibility.